ALEKS Subject Test

Mathematics

Student Practice Workbook

+ Two Full-Length ALEKS Math Tests

Math Notion

www.MathNotion.com

ALEKS Subject Test Mathematics

Published in the United State of America By

The Math Notion

Web: WWW.MathNotion.com

Email: info@Mathnotion.com

ISBN: 978-1-63620-049-1

The Math Notion

Michael Smith has been a math instructor for over a decade now. He launched the Math Notion. Since 2006, we have devoted our time to both teaching and developing exceptional math learning materials. As a test prep company, we have worked with thousands of students. We have used the feedback of our students to develop a unique study program that can be used by students to drastically improve their math scores fast and effectively. We have more than a thousand Math learning books including:

- **SAT Math Prep**

- **ACT Math Prep**

- **GRE Math Prep**

- **Accuplacer Math Prep**

- **Common Core Math Prep**

- **many Math Education Workbooks, Study Guides, Practice and Exercise Books**

As an experienced Math test preparation company, we have helped many students raise their standardized test scores—and attend the colleges of their dreams: We tutor online and in person, we teach students in large groups, and we provide training materials and textbooks through our website and through Amazon.

You can contact us via email at:

info@Mathnotion.com

Get the Targeted Practice You Need to Ace the ALEKS Math Test!

ALEKS Subject Test - Mathematics includes easy-to-follow instructions, helpful examples, and plenty of math practice problems to assist students to master each concept, brush up their problem-solving skills, and create confidence.

The ALEKS math practice book provides numerous opportunities to evaluate basic skills along with abundant remediation and intervention activities. It is a skill that permits you to quickly master intricate information and produce better leads in less time.

Students can boost their test-taking skills by taking the book's two practice ALEKS Math exams. All test questions answered and explained in detail.

Important Features of the ALEKS Math Book:

- A **complete review** of ALEKS math test topics,
- Over 2,500 practice problems covering all topics tested,
- The most important concepts you need to know,
- Clear and concise, easy-to-follow sections,
- Well designed for enhanced learning and interest,
- Hands-on experience with all question types
- **2 full-length practice tests** with detailed answer explanations
- Cost-Effective Pricing

Powerful math exercises to help you avoid traps and pacing yourself to beat the ALEKS test. Students will gain valuable experience and raise their confidence by taking math practice tests, learning about test structure, and gaining a deeper understanding of what is tested on the ALEKS Math. If ever there was a book to respond to the pressure to increase students' test scores, this is it.

WWW.MathNotion.COM

… So Much More Online!

✓ FREE Math Lessons

✓ More Math Learning Books!

✓ Mathematics Worksheets

✓ Online Math Tutors

For a PDF Version of This Book

Please Visit WWW.MathNotion.com

Contents

Chapter 1 :

Integers and Number Theory

Topics that you will practice in this chapter:

- ✓ Rounding
- ✓ Rounding and Estimates
- ✓ Adding and Subtracting Integers
- ✓ Multiplying and Dividing Integers
- ✓ Order of Operations
- ✓ Ordering Integers and Numbers
- ✓ Integers and Absolute Value
- ✓ Factoring Numbers
- ✓ Greatest Common Factor (GCF)
- ✓ Least Common Multiple (LCM)
- ✓ Sets

"Wherever there is number, there is beauty." –*Proclus*

Rounding

✍ **Round each number to the nearest ten.**

1) 42 = ____   5) 19 = ____   9) 48 = ____

2) 88 = ____   6) 25 = ____   10) 81 = ____

3) 24 = ____   7) 93 = ____   11) 58 = ____

4) 57 = ____   8) 71 = ____   12) 87 = ____

✍ **Round each number to the nearest hundred.**

13) 198 = ____   17) 321 = ____   21) 580 = ____

14) 387 = ____   18) 433 = ____   22) 868 = ____

15) 816 = ____   19) 579 = ____   23) 480 = ____

16) 101 = ____   20) 825 = ____   24) 287 = ____

✍ **Round each number to the nearest thousand.**

25) 1,382 = ____   29) 9,099 = ____   33) 52,866 = ____

26) 3,420 = ____   30) 22,980 = ____   34) 85,190 = ____

27) 4,254 = ____   31) 45,188 = ____   35) 70,990 = ____

28) 6,861 = ____   32) 16,808 = ____   36) 26,869 = ____

Rounding and Estimates

✎ **Estimate the sum by rounding each number to the nearest ten.**

1) $13 + 22 =$ _____

2) $71 + 23 =$ _____

3) $61 + 58 =$ _____

4) $56 + 85 =$ _____

5) $368 + 249 =$ _____

6) $330 + 903 =$ _____

7) $471 + 293 =$ _____

8) $1,950 + 2,655 =$ _____

✎ **Estimate the product by rounding each number to the nearest ten.**

9) $32 \times 71 =$ _____

10) $12 \times 33 =$ _____

11) $31 \times 83 =$ _____

12) $19 \times 11 =$ _____

13) $42 \times 76 =$ _____

14) $63 \times 34 =$ _____

15) $19 \times 31 =$ _____

16) $59 \times 71 =$ _____

✎ **Estimate the sum or product by rounding each number to the nearest ten.**

17) $\begin{array}{r} 29 \\ \times\ 12 \\ \hline \end{array}$

18) $\begin{array}{r} 37 \\ \times\ 26 \\ \hline \end{array}$

19) $\begin{array}{r} 48 \\ +\ 82 \\ \hline \end{array}$

20) $\begin{array}{r} 65 \\ +44 \\ \hline \end{array}$

21) $\begin{array}{r} 37 \\ \times\ 14 \\ \hline \end{array}$

22) $\begin{array}{r} 71 \\ +\ 32 \\ \hline \end{array}$

Adding and Subtracting Integers

✎ **Find each sum.**

1) $14 + (-6) =$

2) $(-13) + (-20) =$

3) $5 + (-28) =$

4) $50 + (-12) =$

5) $(-7) + (-15) + 3 =$

6) $30 + (-14) + 8 =$

7) $40 + (-10) + (-14) + 17 =$

8) $(-15) + (-20) + 13 + 35 =$

9) $40 + (-20) + (38 - 29) =$

10) $28 + (-12) + (30 - 12) =$

✎ **Find each difference.**

11) $(-18) - (-7) =$

12) $25 - (-14) =$

13) $(-20) - 36 =$

14) $34 - (-19) =$

15) $51 - (30 - 21) =$

16) $17 - (5) - (-24) =$

17) $(35 + 20) - (-46) =$

18) $48 - 16 - (-8) =$

19) $62 - (28 + 17) - (-15) =$

20) $58 - (-23) - (-31) =$

21) $19 - (-8) - (-13) =$

22) $(19 - 24) - (-14) =$

23) $27 - 33 - (-21) =$

24) $58 - (32 + 24) - (-9) =$

25) $36 - (-30) + (-17) =$

26) $27 - (-42) + (-31) =$

Multiplying and Dividing Integers

✎ **Find each product.**

1) $(-9) \times (-5) =$

2) $(-3) \times 9 =$

3) $8 \times (-12) =$

4) $(-7) \times (-20) =$

5) $(-3) \times (-5) \times 6 =$

6) $(14 - 3) \times (-8) =$

7) $12 \times (-9) \times (-3) =$

8) $(140 + 10) \times (-2) =$

9) $10 \times (-12 + 8) \times 3 =$

10) $(-8) \times (-5) \times (-10) =$

✎ **Find each quotient.**

11) $42 \div (-7) =$

12) $(-48) \div (-6) =$

13) $(-40) \div (-8) =$

14) $54 \div (-2) =$

15) $152 \div 19 =$

16) $(-144) \div (-12) =$

17) $180 \div (-10) =$

18) $(-312) \div (-12) =$

19) $221 \div (-13) =$

20) $(-126) \div (6) =$

21) $(-161) \div (-7) =$

22) $-266 \div (-14) =$

23) $(-120) \div (-4) =$

24) $270 \div (-18) =$

25) $(-208) \div (-8) =$

26) $(135) \div (-15) =$

Order of Operations

✎ **Evaluate each expression.**

1) $7 + (5 \times 4) =$

2) $14 - (3 \times 6) =$

3) $(19 \times 4) + 16 =$

4) $(16 - 7) - (8 \times 2) =$

5) $27 + (18 \div 3) =$

6) $(18 \times 8) \div 6 =$

7) $(32 \div 4) \times (-2) =$

8) $(9 \times 4) + (32 - 18) =$

9) $24 + (4 \times 3) + 7 =$

10) $(36 \times 3) \div (2 + 2) =$

11) $(-7) + (12 \times 3) + 11 =$

12) $(8 \times 5) - (24 \div 6) =$

13) $(7 \times 6 \div 3) - (12 + 9) =$

14) $(13 + 5 - 14) \times 3 - 2 =$

15) $(20 - 14 + 30) \times (64 \div 4) =$

16) $32 + \left(28 - (36 \div 9)\right) =$

17) $(7 + 6 - 4 - 7) + (15 \div 5) =$

18) $(85 - 20) + (20 - 18 + 7) =$

19) $(20 \times 2) + (14 \times 3) - 22 =$

20) $18 + 5 - (30 \times 3) + 20 =$

Ordering Integers and Numbers

✎ **Order each set of integers from least to greatest.**

1) $8, -10, -5, -3, 4$ ___ , ___ , ___ , ___ , ___ , ___

2) $-10, -18, 6, 14, 27$ ___ , ___ , ___ , ___ , ___ , ___

3) $15, -8, -21, 21, -23$ ___ , ___ , ___ , ___ , ___ , ___

4) $-14, -40, 23, -12, 47$ ___ , ___ , ___ , ___ , ___ , ___

5) $59, -54, 32, -57, 36$ ___ , ___ , ___ , ___ , ___ , ___

6) $68, 26, -19, 47, -34$ ___ , ___ , ___ , ___ , ___ , ___

✎ **Order each set of integers from greatest to least.**

7) $18, 36, -16, -18, -10$ ___ , ___ , ___ , ___ , ___ , ___

8) $27, 34, -12, -24, 94$ ___ , ___ , ___ , ___ , ___ , ___

9) $50, -21, -13, 42, -2$ ___ , ___ , ___ , ___ , ___ , ___

10) $37, 46, -20, -16, 86$ ___ , ___ , ___ , ___ , ___ , ___

11) $-18, 88, -26, -59, 75$ ___ , ___ , ___ , ___ , ___ , ___

12) $-65, -30, -25, 3, 14$ ___ , ___ , ___ , ___ , ___ , ___

Integers and Absolute Value

✍ **Write absolute value of each number.**

1) $|-2| =$

2) $|-27| =$

3) $|-20| =$

4) $|14| =$

5) $|6| =$

6) $|-55| =$

7) $|16| =$

8) $|2| =$

9) $|54| =$

10) $|-4| =$

11) $|-11|$

12) $|88| =$

13) $|0| =$

14) $|79| =$

15) $|-32| =$

16) $|-17| =$

17) $|42| =$

18) $|-46| =$

19) $|1| =$

20) $|-40| =$

✍ **Evaluate the value.**

21) $|-5| - \frac{|-21|}{7} =$

22) $14 - |3 - 15| - |-4| =$

23) $\frac{|-32|}{4} \times |-4| =$

24) $\frac{|7 \times (-3)|}{7} \times \frac{|-19|}{3} =$

25) $|4 \times (-5)| + \frac{|-40|}{5} =$

26) $\frac{|-45|}{9} \times \frac{|-24|}{12} =$

27) $|-12 + 8| \times \frac{|-7 \times 7|}{7}$

28) $\frac{|-11 \times 2|}{4} \times |-16| =$

Factoring Numbers

✎ **List all positive factors of each number.**

1) 9

2) 16

3) 24

4) 30

5) 26

6) 46

7) 20

8) 68

9) 28

10) 98

11) 14

12) 54

13) 55

14) 18

15) 63

16) 34

17) 50

18) 62

19) 95

20) 64

21) 70

22) 45

23) 22

24) 65

Greatest Common Factor

Find the GCF for each number pair.

1) 6, 2

2) 4, 5

3) 3, 12

4) 7, 3

5) 5, 10

6) 8, 48

7) 6, 18

8) 9, 15

9) 12, 18

10) 4, 36

11) 6, 10

12) 28, 52

13) 25, 10

14) 22, 24

15) 9, 54

16) 8, 54

17) 42, 14

18) 16, 40

19) 9, 2, 3

20) 5, 15, 10

21) 7, 9, 2

22) 16, 64

23) 30, 48

24) 36, 63

Least Common Multiple

✎ **Find the LCM for each number pair.**

1) 6, 9

2) 15, 45

3) 16, 40

4) 12, 36

5) 18, 27

6) 14, 42

7) 6, 30

8) 8, 56

9) 7, 21

10) 8, 20

11) 15, 25

12) 7, 9

13) 4, 11

14) 8, 28

15) 28, 56

16) 40, 50

17) 12, 13

18) 22, 11

19) 36, 20

20) 15, 35

21) 18, 81

22) 30, 54

23) 18, 45

24) 75, 25

Sets

✎ Given A = {3, 4, 5, 7, 13}, B = {1, 6, 9, 10}, and C = {4, 6, 7, 10}, find:

1) A ∪ C _____   6) A ∩ C _____

2) A ∪ B _____   7) (C ∪ B) ∪ A _____

3) B ∪ C _____   8) (A ∪ C) ∩ B _____

4) C ∩ B _____   9) (C ∩ B) ∩ A _____

5) A ∩ B _____   10) (B ∪ A) ∩ C _____

✎ **Refer to the diagram below to find each set.**

11) A ∪ B _____

12) A ∪ C _____

13) C ∪ B _____

14) A ∩ C _____

15) B ∩ C _____

16) B ∩ A _____

17) (A ∪ C) ∪ B _____

18) (C ∪ B) ∩ A _____

19) (A ∩ B) ∩ C _____

20) (A ∪ C) ∩ B _____

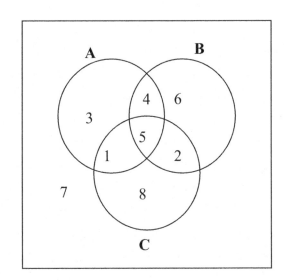

Answers of Worksheets

Rounding

1) 40	10) 80	19) 600	28) 7,000
2) 90	11) 60	20) 800	29) 9,000
3) 20	12) 90	21) 600	30) 23,000
4) 60	13) 200	22) 900	31) 45,000
5) 20	14) 400	23) 500	32) 17,000
6) 30	15) 800	24) 300	33) 53,000
7) 90	16) 100	25) 1,000	34) 85,000
8) 70	17) 300	26) 3,000	35) 71,000
9) 50	18) 400	27) 4,000	36) 27,000

Rounding and Estimates

1) 30	7) 760	13) 3,200	19) 130
2) 90	8) 4,610	14) 1,800	20) 110
3) 120	9) 2,100	15) 600	21) 400
4) 150	10) 300	16) 4,200	22) 100
5) 620	11) 2,400	17) 300	
6) 1,230	12) 200	18) 1,200	

Adding and Subtracting Integers

1) 8	8) 13	15) 42	22) 9
2) −33	9) 29	16) 36	23) 15
3) −23	10) 34	17) 101	24) 11
4) 38	11) −11	18) 40	25) 49
5) −19	12) 39	19) 32	26) 38
6) 24	13) −56	20) 112	
7) 33	14) 53	21) 40	

Multiplying and Dividing Integers

1) 45	6) −88	11) −6	16) 12
2) −27	7) 324	12) 8	17) −18
3) −96	8) −300	13) 5	18) 26
4) 140	9) −120	14) −27	19) −17
5) 90	10) −400	15) 8	20) −21

21) 23	23) 30	25) 26
22) 19	24) −15	26) −9

Order of Operations

1) 27	6) 24	11) 40	16) 56
2) −4	7) −16	12) 36	17) 5
3) 92	8) 50	13) −7	18) 74
4) −7	9) 43	14) 10	19) 60
5) 33	10) 27	15) 576	20) −47

Ordering Integers and Numbers

1) −10, −5, −3, 4, 8	7) 36, 18, −10, −16, −18
2) −18, −10, 6, 14, 27	8) 94, 34, 27, −12, −24
3) −23, −21, −8, 15, 21	9) 50, 42, −2, −13, −21
4) −40, −14, −12, 23, 47	10) 86, 46, 37, −16, −20
5) −57, −54, 32, 36, 59	11) 88, 75, −18, −26, −59
6) −34, −19, 26, 47, 68	12) 14, 3, −25, −30, −65

Integers and Absolute Value

1) 2	8) 2	15) 32	22) −2
2) 27	9) 54	16) 17	23) 32
3) 20	10) 4	17) 42	24) 19
4) 14	11) 11	18) 46	25) 28
5) 6	12) 88	19) 1	26) 10
6) 55	13) 0	20) 40	27) 28
7) 16	14) 79	21) 2	28) 88

Factoring Numbers

1) 1, 3, 9	8) 1, 2, 4, 17, 34, 68	15) 1, 3, 7, 9, 21, 63
2) 1, 2, 4, 8, 16	9) 1, 2, 4, 7, 14, 28	16) 1, 2, 17, 34
3) 1, 2, 3, 4, 6, 8, 12, 24	10) 1, 2, 7, 14, 49, 98	17) 1, 2, 5, 10, 25, 50
4) 1, 2, 3, 5, 6, 10, 15, 30	11) 1, 2, 7, 14	18) 1, 2, 31, 62
5) 1, 2, 13, 26	12) 1, 2, 3, 6, 9, 18, 27, 54	19) 1, 5, 19, 95
6) 1, 2, 23, 46	13) 1, 5, 11, 55	20) 1, 2, 4, 8, 16, 32, 64
7) 1, 2, 4, 5, 10, 20	14) 1, 2, 3, 6, 9, 18	21) 1, 2, 5, 7, 10, 14, 35, 70

22) 1, 3, 5, 9, 15, 45   23) 1, 2, 11, 22   24) 1, 5, 13, 65

Greatest Common Factor

1) 2	7) 6	13) 5	19) 1
2) 1	8) 3	14) 2	20) 5
3) 3	9) 6	15) 9	21) 1
4) 1	10) 4	16) 2	22) 16
5) 5	11) 2	17) 14	23) 6
6) 8	12) 4	18) 8	24) 9

Least Common Multiple

1) 18	7) 30	13) 44	19) 180
2) 45	8) 56	14) 56	20) 105
3) 80	9) 21	15) 56	21) 162
4) 36	10) 40	16) 200	22) 270
5) 54	11) 75	17) 156	23) 90
6) 42	12) 63	18) 22	24) 75

Sets

1) {3, 4, 5, 6, 7, 10, 13}	8) {6, 10}	15) {2, 5}
2) {1, 3, 4, 5, 6, 7, 9, 10, 13}	9) { } (empty set)	16) {4, 5}
3) {1, 4, 6, 7, 9, 10}	10) {4, 6, 7, 10}	17) {1, 2, 3, 4, 5, 6, 8}
4) {6, 10}	11) {1, 2, 3, 4, 5, 6}	18) {1, 4, 5}
5) { } (empty set)	12) {1, 2, 3, 4, 5, 8}	19) {5}
6) {4, 7}	13) {1, 2, 4, 5, 6, 8}	20) {2, 4, 5}
7) {1, 3, 4, 5, 6, 7, 9, 10, 13}	14) {1, 5}	

Chapter 2 :

Fractions and Decimals

Topics that you will practice in this chapter:

- ✓ Simplifying Fractions
- ✓ Adding and Subtracting Fractions
- ✓ Multiplying and Dividing Fractions
- ✓ Adding and Subtract Mixed Numbers
- ✓ Multiplying and Dividing Mixed Numbers
- ✓ Adding and Subtracting Decimals
- ✓ Multiplying and Dividing Decimals
- ✓ Comparing Decimals
- ✓ Rounding Decimals

"A Man is like a fraction whose numerator is what he is and whose denominator is what he thinks of himself. The larger the denominator, the smaller the fraction." –Tolstoy

Simplifying Fractions

✍ **Simplify each fraction to its lowest terms.**

1) $\frac{5}{10} =$

2) $\frac{28}{35} =$

3) $\frac{27}{36} =$

4) $\frac{40}{80} =$

5) $\frac{14}{56} =$

6) $\frac{32}{48} =$

7) $\frac{52}{65} =$

8) $\frac{15}{60} =$

9) $\frac{80}{160} =$

10) $\frac{55}{77} =$

11) $\frac{28}{112} =$

12) $\frac{32}{64} =$

13) $\frac{63}{72} =$

14) $\frac{81}{90} =$

15) $\frac{35}{105} =$

16) $\frac{25}{70} =$

17) $\frac{80}{280} =$

18) $\frac{12}{81} =$

19) $\frac{36}{186} =$

20) $\frac{240}{540} =$

21) $\frac{70}{560} =$

✍ **Find the answer for each problem.**

22) Which of the following fractions equal to $\frac{3}{4}$? _____

     A. $\frac{60}{90}$ B. $\frac{43}{104}$ C. $\frac{48}{64}$ D. $\frac{150}{300}$

23) Which of the following fractions equal to $\frac{5}{8}$? _____

     A. $\frac{125}{200}$ B. $\frac{115}{200}$ C. $\frac{50}{100}$ D. $\frac{30}{90}$

24) Which of the following fractions equal to $\frac{3}{7}$? _____

     A. $\frac{58}{116}$ B. $\frac{54}{126}$ C. $\frac{270}{167}$ D. $\frac{42}{63}$

Adding and Subtracting Fractions

✍ **Find the sum.**

1) $\frac{5}{9} + \frac{4}{9} =$

2) $\frac{1}{2} + \frac{1}{7} =$

3) $\frac{3}{8} + \frac{1}{4} =$

4) $\frac{3}{5} + \frac{1}{2} =$

5) $\frac{1}{4} + \frac{3}{5} =$

6) $\frac{7}{8} + \frac{3}{8} =$

7) $\frac{1}{2} + \frac{7}{10} =$

8) $\frac{2}{5} + \frac{2}{3} =$

9) $\frac{5}{7} + \frac{2}{3} =$

10) $\frac{7}{12} + \frac{3}{4} =$

11) $\frac{5}{6} + \frac{2}{5} =$

12) $\frac{1}{12} + \frac{2}{3} =$

✍ **Find the difference.**

13) $\frac{1}{3} - \frac{1}{6} =$

14) $\frac{3}{4} - \frac{1}{8} =$

15) $\frac{1}{2} - \frac{1}{3} =$

16) $\frac{1}{4} - \frac{1}{5} =$

17) $\frac{5}{8} - \frac{2}{3} =$

18) $\frac{1}{4} - \frac{1}{7} =$

19) $\frac{5}{6} - \frac{1}{9} =$

20) $\frac{3}{4} - \frac{1}{6} =$

21) $\frac{7}{8} - \frac{1}{12} =$

22) $\frac{8}{15} - \frac{3}{5} =$

23) $\frac{3}{12} - \frac{1}{14} =$

24) $\frac{10}{13} - \frac{7}{26} =$

25) $\frac{6}{7} - \frac{3}{4} =$

26) $\frac{4}{5} - \frac{1}{8} =$

27) $\frac{4}{7} - \frac{2}{35} =$

28) $\frac{9}{16} - \frac{2}{8} =$

29) $\frac{8}{9} - \frac{7}{18} =$

30) $\frac{1}{2} - \frac{4}{9} =$

Multiplying and Dividing Fractions

✎ Find the value of each expression in lowest terms.

1) $\frac{1}{5} \times \frac{15}{5} =$

5) $\frac{1}{5} \times \frac{1}{4} =$

9) $\frac{5}{8} \times \frac{3}{5} =$

2) $\frac{9}{12} \times \frac{4}{9} =$

6) $\frac{7}{9} \times \frac{1}{7} =$

10) $\frac{4}{7} \times \frac{1}{8} =$

3) $\frac{1}{16} \times \frac{8}{10} =$

7) $\frac{6}{7} \times \frac{1}{3} =$

11) $\frac{7}{15} \times \frac{5}{7} =$

4) $\frac{1}{24} \times \frac{8}{10} =$

8) $\frac{2}{8} \times \frac{2}{8} =$

12) $\frac{3}{10} \times \frac{5}{9} =$

✎ Find the value of each expression in lowest terms.

13) $\frac{1}{4} \div \frac{1}{8} =$

19) $\frac{2}{7} \div \frac{7}{13} =$

25) $\frac{1}{9} \div \frac{2}{5} =$

14) $\frac{1}{10} \div \frac{1}{5} =$

20) $\frac{1}{24} \div \frac{3}{16} =$

26) $\frac{5}{12} \div \frac{3}{5} =$

15) $\frac{3}{4} \div \frac{1}{5} =$

21) $\frac{7}{12} \div \frac{5}{6} =$

27) $\frac{3}{20} \div \frac{1}{6} =$

16) $\frac{1}{3} \div \frac{5}{6} =$

22) $\frac{22}{18} \div \frac{11}{9} =$

28) $\frac{8}{20} \div \frac{3}{4} =$

17) $\frac{1}{7} \div \frac{8}{42} =$

23) $\frac{9}{35} \div \frac{3}{7} =$

29) $\frac{5}{6} \div \frac{2}{9} =$

18) $\frac{3}{4} \div \frac{1}{6} =$

24) $\frac{2}{7} \div \frac{8}{21} =$

30) $\frac{5}{11} \div \frac{3}{4} =$

Adding and Subtracting Mixed Numbers

✎ Find the sum.

1) $3\frac{1}{3} + 2\frac{1}{6} =$

2) $4\frac{1}{2} + 3\frac{1}{2} =$

3) $3\frac{3}{8} + 1\frac{1}{8} =$

4) $2\frac{1}{4} + 2\frac{1}{3} =$

5) $3\frac{5}{6} + 2\frac{7}{12} =$

6) $5\frac{4}{15} + 3\frac{3}{5} =$

7) $2\frac{1}{3} + 4\frac{3}{7} =$

8) $3\frac{1}{2} + 4\frac{2}{5} =$

9) $5\frac{2}{5} + 6\frac{3}{7} =$

10) $8\frac{5}{16} + 6\frac{1}{12} =$

✎ Find the difference.

11) $3\frac{1}{4} - 1\frac{3}{4} =$

12) $6\frac{3}{5} - 4\frac{2}{5} =$

13) $4\frac{1}{3} - 3\frac{1}{9} =$

14) $7\frac{1}{7} - 5\frac{1}{2} =$

15) $5\frac{1}{3} - 2\frac{1}{12} =$

16) $8\frac{1}{5} - 4\frac{1}{3} =$

17) $9\frac{1}{4} - 6\frac{1}{8} =$

18) $11\frac{7}{15} - 8\frac{3}{5} =$

19) $14\frac{5}{6} - 11\frac{3}{5} =$

20) $18\frac{2}{7} - 14\frac{1}{5} =$

21) $9\frac{1}{3} - 4\frac{1}{4} =$

22) $6\frac{1}{8} - 4\frac{1}{16} =$

23) $19\frac{3}{8} - 15\frac{1}{3} =$

24) $11\frac{1}{9} - 8\frac{1}{8} =$

25) $17\frac{1}{7} - 11\frac{1}{5} =$

26) $16\frac{2}{9} - 9\frac{5}{7} =$

Multiplying and Dividing Mixed Numbers

🖎 **Find the product.**

1) $5\frac{1}{2} \times 2\frac{1}{4} =$

2) $5\frac{1}{3} \times 4\frac{1}{3} =$

3) $5\frac{3}{4} \times 6\frac{1}{4} =$

4) $3\frac{1}{3} \times 2\frac{3}{5} =$

5) $4\frac{8}{10} \times 1\frac{1}{24} =$

6) $6\frac{2}{7} \times 1\frac{1}{11} =$

7) $8\frac{2}{3} \times 3\frac{1}{2} =$

8) $3\frac{4}{7} \times 2\frac{1}{5} =$

9) $5\frac{2}{8} \times 4\frac{1}{6} =$

10) $7\frac{3}{3} \times 1\frac{3}{8} =$

🖎 **Find the quotient.**

11) $2\frac{2}{5} \div 4\frac{1}{5} =$

12) $4\frac{1}{6} \div 3\frac{1}{3} =$

13) $6\frac{1}{3} \div 1\frac{1}{2} =$

14) $7\frac{1}{10} \div 2\frac{2}{5} =$

15) $3\frac{1}{3} \div 1\frac{1}{9} =$

16) $1\frac{1}{10} \div 4\frac{1}{2} =$

17) $1\frac{3}{16} \div 5\frac{1}{4} =$

18) $4\frac{1}{3} \div 4\frac{3}{4} =$

19) $9\frac{1}{3} \div 2\frac{1}{4} =$

20) $15\frac{1}{3} \div 5\frac{1}{2} =$

21) $4\frac{1}{6} \div 1\frac{1}{5} =$

22) $1\frac{1}{18} \div 1\frac{2}{9} =$

23) $4\frac{2}{7} \div 1\frac{3}{10} =$

24) $7\frac{1}{3} \div 2\frac{2}{11} =$

25) $8\frac{2}{5} \div 1\frac{1}{6} =$

26) $9\frac{1}{3} \div 2\frac{1}{7} =$

Adding and Subtracting Decimals

✎ **Add and subtract decimals.**

$$
\begin{array}{r}
35.19 \\
- \ 24.28 \\
\hline
\end{array}
$$
1)

$$
\begin{array}{r}
38.72 \\
- \ 21.68 \\
\hline
\end{array}
$$
4)

$$
\begin{array}{r}
86.09 \\
- \ 35.14 \\
\hline
\end{array}
$$
7)

$$
\begin{array}{r}
34.29 \\
+ \ 42.58 \\
\hline
\end{array}
$$
2)

$$
\begin{array}{r}
57.39 \\
+ \ 26.54 \\
\hline
\end{array}
$$
5)

$$
\begin{array}{r}
54.51 \\
+ \ 32.66 \\
\hline
\end{array}
$$
8)

$$
\begin{array}{r}
61.20 \\
+ \ 33.75 \\
\hline
\end{array}
$$
3)

$$
\begin{array}{r}
70.24 \\
- \ 42.35 \\
\hline
\end{array}
$$
6)

$$
\begin{array}{r}
114.21 \\
- \ 88.69 \\
\hline
\end{array}
$$
9)

✎ **Find the missing number.**

10) ___ $+ \ 2.8 = 5.4$

11) $4.1 +$ ___ $= 5.88$

12) $6.45 +$ ___ $= 8$

13) $7.25 -$ ___ $= 3.40$

14) ___ $- \ 2.35 = 4.25$

15) ___ $- \ 19.85 = 6.54$

16) $22.15 +$ ___ $= 28.95$

17) ___ $- \ 37.16 = 9.42$

18) ___ $+ \ 24.50 = 34.19$

19) $72.40 +$ ___ $= 125.20$

Multiplying and Dividing Decimals

✍ **Find the product.**

1) $0.5 \times 0.6 =$

2) $3.3 \times 0.4 =$

3) $1.28 \times 0.5 =$

4) $0.35 \times 0.6 =$

5) $1.85 \times 0.6 =$

6) $0.24 \times 0.5 =$

7) $5.25 \times 1.4 =$

8) $18.5 \times 4.6 =$

9) $15.4 \times 6.8 =$

10) $19.5 \times 2.6 =$

11) $32.2 \times 1.5 =$

12) $78.4 \times 4.5 =$

✍ **Find the quotient.**

13) $1.85 \div 10 =$

14) $74.6 \div 100 =$

15) $3.6 \div 3 =$

16) $9.6 \div 0.4 =$

17) $15.5 \div 0.5 =$

18) $32.8 \div 0.2 =$

19) $22.15 \div 1,000 =$

20) $53.55 \div 0.7 =$

21) $322.2 \div 0.2 =$

22) $50.67 \div 0.18 =$

23) $77.4 \div 0.8 =$

24) $27.93 \div 0.03 =$

Comparing Decimals

✎ **Write the correct comparison symbol (>, < or =).**

1) 0.70 ☐ 0.070

2) 0.049 ☐ 0.49

3) 5.090 ☐ 5.09

4) 2.57 ☐ 2.05

5) 9.03 ☐ 0.930

6) 6.06 ☐ 6.6

7) 7.02 ☐ 7.020

8) 3.04 ☐ 3.2

9) 3.61 ☐ 3.245

10) 0.986 ☐ 0.0986

11) 17.24 ☐ 17.240

12) 0.759 ☐ 0.81

13) 9.040 ☐ 9.40

14) 5.73 ☐ 5.213

15) 9.44 ☐ 9.404

16) 7.17 ☐ 7.170

17) 4.85 ☐ 4.085

18) 9.041 ☐ 9.40

19) 3.033 ☐ 3.030

20) 4.97 ☐ 4.970

Rounding Decimals

✎ **Round each decimal to the nearest whole number.**

1) 28.12	3) 16.22	5) 7.95
2) 6.9	4) 8.5	6) 52.7

✎ **Round each decimal to the nearest tenth.**

7) 31.761	9) 94.729	11) 13.219
8) 14.421	10) 77.89	12) 59.89

✎ **Round each decimal to the nearest hundredth.**

13) 8.428	15) 55.3786	17) 62.241
14) 23.812	16) 231.912	18) 19.447

✎ **Round each decimal to the nearest thousandth.**

19) 15.54324	21) 243.8652	23) 67.1983
20) 34.62586	22) 80.4529	24) 72.36788

Answers of Worksheets

Simplifying Fractions

1) $\frac{1}{2}$

2) $\frac{4}{5}$

3) $\frac{3}{4}$

4) $\frac{1}{2}$

5) $\frac{1}{4}$

6) $\frac{2}{3}$

7) $\frac{4}{5}$

8) $\frac{1}{4}$

9) $\frac{1}{2}$

10) $\frac{5}{7}$

11) $\frac{1}{4}$

12) $\frac{1}{2}$

13) $\frac{7}{8}$

14) $\frac{9}{10}$

15) $\frac{1}{3}$

16) $\frac{5}{14}$

17) $\frac{2}{7}$

18) $\frac{4}{27}$

19) $\frac{6}{31}$

20) $\frac{4}{9}$

21) $\frac{1}{8}$

22) C

23) A

24) B

Adding and Subtracting Fractions

1) $\frac{9}{9} = 1$

2) $\frac{9}{14}$

3) $\frac{5}{8}$

4) $1\frac{1}{10}$

5) $\frac{17}{20}$

6) $1\frac{1}{4}$

7) $1\frac{1}{5}$

8) $1\frac{1}{15}$

9) $1\frac{8}{21}$

10) $1\frac{1}{3}$

11) $1\frac{7}{30}$

12) $\frac{3}{4}$

13) $\frac{1}{6}$

14) $\frac{5}{8}$

15) $\frac{1}{6}$

16) $\frac{1}{20}$

17) $-\frac{1}{24}$

18) $\frac{3}{28}$

19) $\frac{13}{18}$

20) $\frac{7}{12}$

21) $\frac{19}{24}$

22) $-\frac{1}{15}$

23) $\frac{5}{28}$

24) $\frac{1}{2}$

25) $\frac{3}{28}$

26) $\frac{27}{40}$

27) $\frac{18}{35}$

28) $\frac{5}{16}$

29) $\frac{1}{2}$

30) $\frac{1}{18}$

Multiplying and Dividing Fractions

1) $\frac{3}{5}$

2) $\frac{1}{3}$

3) $\frac{1}{20}$

4) $\frac{1}{30}$

5) $\frac{1}{20}$

6) $\frac{1}{9}$

7) $\frac{2}{7}$

8) $\frac{1}{16}$

9) $\frac{3}{8}$

10) $\frac{1}{14}$

11) $\frac{1}{3}$

12) $\frac{1}{6}$

13) 2

14) $\frac{1}{2}$

15) $3\frac{3}{4}$

16) $\frac{2}{5}$

17) $\frac{3}{4}$

18) $4\frac{1}{2}$

19) $\frac{26}{49}$

20) $\frac{2}{9}$

21) $\frac{7}{10}$

22) 1

23) $\frac{3}{5}$

24) $\frac{3}{4}$

25) $\frac{5}{18}$

26) $\frac{25}{36}$ 28) $\frac{8}{15}$ 30) $\frac{20}{33}$

27) $\frac{9}{10}$ 29) $3\frac{3}{4}$

Adding and Subtracting Mixed Numbers

1) $5\frac{1}{2}$ 8) $7\frac{9}{10}$ 15) $3\frac{1}{4}$ 22) $2\frac{1}{16}$

2) 8 9) $11\frac{29}{35}$ 16) $3\frac{13}{15}$ 23) $4\frac{1}{24}$

3) $4\frac{1}{2}$ 10) $14\frac{19}{48}$ 17) $3\frac{1}{8}$ 24) $2\frac{71}{72}$

4) $4\frac{7}{12}$ 11) $1\frac{1}{2}$ 18) $2\frac{13}{15}$ 25) $5\frac{33}{35}$

5) $6\frac{5}{12}$ 12) $2\frac{1}{5}$ 19) $3\frac{7}{30}$ 26) $6\frac{32}{63}$

6) $8\frac{13}{15}$ 13) $1\frac{2}{9}$ 20) $4\frac{3}{35}$

7) $6\frac{16}{21}$ 14) $1\frac{9}{14}$ 21) $5\frac{1}{12}$

Multiplying and Dividing Mixed Numbers

1) $12\frac{3}{8}$ 10) 11 19) $4\frac{4}{27}$

2) $23\frac{1}{9}$ 11) $\frac{4}{7}$ 20) $2\frac{26}{33}$

3) $35\frac{15}{16}$ 12) $1\frac{1}{4}$ 21) $3\frac{17}{36}$

4) $8\frac{2}{3}$ 13) $4\frac{2}{9}$ 22) $\frac{19}{22}$

5) 5 14) $2\frac{23}{24}$ 23) $3\frac{27}{91}$

6) $6\frac{6}{7}$ 15) 3 24) $3\frac{13}{36}$

7) $30\frac{1}{3}$ 16) $\frac{11}{45}$ 25) $7\frac{1}{5}$

8) $7\frac{6}{7}$ 17) $\frac{19}{84}$ 26) $4\frac{16}{45}$

9) $21\frac{7}{8}$ 18) $\frac{52}{57}$

Adding and Subtracting Decimals

1) 10.91   6) 27.89   11) 1.78   16) 6.8

2) 76.87   7) 50.95   12) 1.55   17) 46.58

3) 94.95   8) 87.17   13) 3.85   18) 9.69

4) 17.04   9) 25.52   14) 6.6   19) 52.8

5) 83.93   10) 2.6   15) 26.39

ALEKS Subject Test Mathematics

Multiplying and Dividing Decimals

1) 0.3
2) 1.32
3) 0.64
4) 0.21
5) 1.11
6) 0.12

7) 7.35
8) 85.1
9) 104.72
10) 50.7
11) 48.3
12) 352.8

13) 0.185
14) 0.746
15) 1.2
16) 24
17) 31
18) 164

19) 0.02215
20) 76.5
21) 1,611
22) 281.5
23) 96.75
24) 931

Comparing Decimals

1) >
2) <
3) =
4) >
5) >

6) <
7) =
8) <
9) >
10) >

11) =
12) <
13) <
14) >
15) >

16) =
17) >
18) <
19) >
20) =

Rounding Decimals

1) 28
2) 7
3) 16
4) 9
5) 8
6) 53
7) 31.8
8) 14.4

9) 94.7
10) 77.9
11) 13.2
12) 59.9
13) 8.43
14) 23.81
15) 55.38
16) 231.91

17) 62.24
18) 19.45
19) 15.543
20) 34.626
21) 243.865
22) 80.453
23) 67.198
24) 72.368

Chapter 3 :

Proportions, Ratios, and Percent

Topics that you will practice in this chapter:

- ✓ Simplifying Ratios
- ✓ Proportional Ratios
- ✓ Similarity and Ratios
- ✓ Ratio and Rates Word Problems
- ✓ Percentage Calculations
- ✓ Percent Problems
- ✓ Discount, Tax and Tip
- ✓ Percent of Change
- ✓ Simple Interest

Without mathematics, there's nothing you can do. Everything around you is mathematics.
Everything around you is numbers." – Shakuntala Devi

Simplifying Ratios

✍ **Reduce each ratio.**

1) $15 : 20 = \underline{} : \underline{}$

2) $7 : 70 = \underline{} : \underline{}$

3) $16 : 28 = \underline{} : \underline{}$

4) $7 : 21 = \underline{} : \underline{}$

5) $4 : 40 = \underline{} : \underline{}$

6) $6 : 48 = \underline{} : \underline{}$

7) $16 : 64 = \underline{} : \underline{}$

8) $10 : 25 = \underline{} : \underline{}$

9) $8 : 48 = \underline{} : \underline{}$

10) $49 : 63 = \underline{} : \underline{}$

11) $18 : 27 = \underline{} : \underline{}$

12) $35 : 10 = \underline{} : \underline{}$

13) $90 : 9 = \underline{} : \underline{}$

14) $24 : 32 = \underline{} : \underline{}$

15) $7 : 56 = \underline{} : \underline{}$

16) $45 : 63 = \underline{} : \underline{}$

17) $56 : 72 = \underline{} : \underline{}$

18) $26 : 13 = \underline{} : \underline{}$

19) $15 : 45 = \underline{} : \underline{}$

20) $28 : 4 = \underline{} : \underline{}$

21) $24 : 48 = \underline{} : \underline{}$

22) $30 : 24 = \underline{} : \underline{}$

23) $70 : 140 = \underline{} : \underline{}$

24) $6 : 180 = \underline{} : \underline{}$

✍ **Write each ratio as a fraction in simplest form.**

25) $6 : 12 =$

26) $30 : 50 =$

27) $15 : 35 =$

28) $9 : 27 =$

29) $8 : 24 =$

30) $18 : 84 =$

31) $7 : 14 =$

32) $7 : 35 =$

33) $40 : 96 =$

34) $12 : 54 =$

35) $44 : 52 =$

36) $12 : 27 =$

37) $15 : 180 =$

38) $39 : 143 =$

39) $20 : 300 =$

40) $30 : 120 =$

41) $56 : 42 =$

42) $26 : 130 =$

43) $66 : 123 =$

44) $70 : 630 =$

45) $75 : 125 =$

Proportional Ratios

✏️ **Fill in the blanks; Calculate each proportion.**

1) $3:8 = $ __ $: 48$

2) $2:5 = 20:$ __

3) $1:9 = $ __ $:81$

4) $6:7 = 12:$ __

5) $9:2 = 63:$ __

6) $8:7 = $ __ $:49$

7) $20:3 = $ __ $:15$

8) $1:3 = $ __ $:75$

9) $7:6 = $ __ $:60$

10) $8:5 = $ __ $:45$

11) $3:10 = 60:$ __

12) $6:11 = 42:$ __

✏️ **State if each pair of ratios form a proportion.**

13) $\frac{3}{20}$ and $\frac{9}{60}$

14) $\frac{1}{7}$ and $\frac{6}{42}$

15) $\frac{3}{7}$ and $\frac{24}{56}$

16) $\frac{4}{9}$ and $\frac{12}{18}$

17) $\frac{1}{9}$ and $\frac{12}{81}$

18) $\frac{7}{8}$ and $\frac{21}{28}$

19) $\frac{9}{13}$ and $\frac{27}{39}$

20) $\frac{1}{8}$ and $\frac{8}{64}$

21) $\frac{6}{19}$ and $\frac{30}{85}$

22) $\frac{5}{9}$ and $\frac{40}{81}$

23) $\frac{9}{14}$ and $\frac{108}{168}$

24) $\frac{15}{23}$ and $\frac{360}{552}$

✏️ **Calculate each proportion.**

25) $\frac{20}{25} = \frac{32}{x}, x = $ ____

26) $\frac{1}{8} = \frac{32}{x}, x = $ ____

27) $\frac{15}{5} = \frac{21}{x}, x = $ ____

28) $\frac{1}{7} = \frac{x}{294}, x = $ ____

29) $\frac{7}{9} = \frac{x}{81}, x = $ ____

30) $\frac{1}{5} = \frac{13}{x}, x = $ ____

31) $\frac{9}{5} = \frac{36}{x}, x = $ ____

32) $\frac{6}{13} = \frac{48}{x}, x = $ ____

33) $\frac{5}{8} = \frac{x}{88}, x = $ ____

34) $\frac{4}{15} = \frac{x}{240}, x = $ ____

35) $\frac{9}{19} = \frac{x}{266}, x = $ ____

36) $\frac{7}{15} = \frac{x}{270}, x = $ ____

Similarity and Ratios

✎ **Each pair of figures is similar. Find the missing side.**

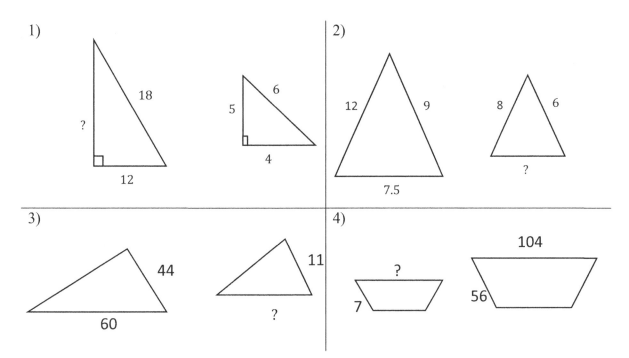

1)

18

5   6

?

4

12

2)

12   9

7.5

8   6

?

3)

44

60

11

?

4)

104

?

7   56

✎ **Calculate.**

5) Two rectangles are similar. The first is 24 feet wide and 120 feet long. The second is 30 feet wide. What is the length of the second rectangle? _____

6) Two rectangles are similar. One is 5 meters by 36 meters. The longer side of the second rectangle is 90 meters. What is the other side of the second rectangle? _____

7) A building casts a shadow 25 ft long. At the same time a girl 10 ft tall casts a shadow 5 ft long. How tall is the building? _____

8) The scale of a map of Texas is 4 inches: 32 miles. If you measure the distance from Dallas to Martin County as 38.4 inches, approximately how far is Martin County from Dallas? _____

Ratio and Rates Word Problems

✍ **Find the answer for each word problem.**

1) Mason has 24 red cards and 36 green cards. What is the ratio of Mason 's red cards to his green cards? _____

2) In a party, 45 soft drinks are required for every 54 guests. If there are 378 guests, how many soft drinks is required? _____

3) In Mason's class, 42 of the students are tall and 24 are short. In Michael's class 84 students are tall and 48 students are short. Which class has a higher ratio of tall to short students? _____

4) The price of 5 apples at the Quick Market is $4.6. The price of 7 of the same apples at Walmart is $5.95. Which place is the better buy? _____

5) The bakers at a Bakery can make 90 bagels in 3 hours. How many bagels can they bake in 24 hours? What is that rate per hour? _____

6) You can buy 5 cans of green beans at a supermarket for $5.75. How much does it cost to buy 45 cans of green beans? _____

7) The ratio of boys to girls in a class is 4: 7. If there are 32 boys in the class, how many girls are in that class? _____

8) The ratio of red marbles to blue marbles in a bag is 3: 7. If there are 50 marbles in the bag, how many of the marbles are red? _____

Percentage Calculations

✍ **Calculate the given percent of each value.**

1) 3% of 60 = ____

2) 20% of 32 = ____

3) 4% of 72 = ____

4) 16% of 32 = ____

5) 25% of 124 = ____

6) 35% of 56 = ____

7) 15% of 20 = ____

8) 14% of 150 = ____

9) 80% of 50 = ____

10) 12% of 115 = ____

11) 72% of 250 = ____

12) 52% of 500 = ____

13) 70% of 400 = ____

14) 27% of 145 = ____

15) 90% of 64 = ____

16) 60% of 55 = ____

17) 22% of 210 = ____

18) 8% of 235 = ____

✍ **Calculate the percent of each given value.**

19) ____% of 25 = 5

20) ____% of 40 = 20

21) ____% of 25 = 2

22) ____% of 50 = 16

23) ____% of 250 = 5

24) ____% of 40 = 32

25) ____% of 125 = 20

26) ____% of 700 = 49

27) ____% of 350 = 49

28) ____% of 500 = 210

✍ **Calculate each percent problem.**

29) A Cinema has 250 seats. 60 seats were sold for the current movie. What percent of seats are empty? _____ %

30) There are 68 boys and 92 girls in a class. 75% of the students in the class take the bus to school. How many students do not take the bus to school? ____

Percent Problems

✎ **Calculate each problem.**

1) 9 is what percent of 45? ____%

2) 60 is what percent of 120? ____%

3) 10 is what percent of 200? ____%

4) 15 is what percent of 125? ____%

5) 10 is what percent of 400? ____%

6) 66 is what percent of 55? ____%

7) 40 is what percent of 160? ____%

8) 40 is what percent of 50? ____%

9) 120 is what percent of 800? ____%

10) 78 is what percent of 120? ___%

11) 36 is what percent of 144? ___%

12) 17 is what percent of 85? ___%

13) 90 is what percent of 900? ___%

14) 36 is what percent of 16? ___%

15) 63 is what percent of 14? ___%

16) 18 is what percent of 60? ___%

17) 126 is what percent of 200? ___%

18) 232 is what percent of 40? ___%

✎ **Calculate each percent word problem.**

19) There are 40 employees in a company. On a certain day, 25 were present. What percent showed up for work? ____%

20) A metal bar weighs 60 ounces. 25% of the bar is gold. How many ounces of gold are in the bar? _____

21) A crew is made up of 12 women; the rest are men. If 15% of the crew are women, how many people are in the crew? _____

22) There are 40 students in a class and 8 of them are girls. What percent are boys? ____%

23) The Royals softball team played 400 games and won 280 of them. What percent of the games did they lose? ____%

Discount, Tax and Tip

✎ **Find the selling price of each item.**

1) Original price of a computer: $420

   Tax: 8% Selling price: $_____

2) Original price of a laptop: $280

   Tax: 4% Selling price: $_____

3) Original price of a sofa: $820

   Tax: 5% Selling price: $_____

4) Original price of a car: $15,800

   Tax: 3.6%   Selling price: $_____

5) Original price of a Table: $250

   Tax: 9% Selling price: $_____

6) Original price of a house: $630,000

   Tax: 1.8%   Selling price: $_____

7) Original price of a tablet: $450

   Discount: 30%   Selling price: $____

8) Original price of a chair: $390

   Discount: 8%   Selling price: $____

9) Original price of a book: $75

   Discount: 42%   Selling price: $____

10) Original price of a cellphone: $820

    Discount: 23%   Selling price: $___

11) Food bill: $45

    Tip: 15%   Price: $_____

12) Food bill: $32

    Tipp: 20%   Price: $_____

13) Food bill: $90

    Tip: 35%   Price: $_____

14) Food bill: $42

    Tipp: 12%   Price: $_____

✎ **Find the answer for each word problem.**

15) Nicolas hired a moving company. The company charged $500 for its services, and Nicolas gives the movers a 40% tip. How much does Nicolas tip the movers? $_____

16) Mason has lunch at a restaurant and the cost of his meal is $90. Mason wants to leave a 25% tip. What is Mason's total bill including tip? $_____

17) The sales tax in Texas is 19.80% and an item costs $350. How much is the tax? $_____

18) The price of a table at Best Buy is $680. If the sales tax is 5%, what is the final price of the table including tax? $_____

Percent of Change

✍ **Find each percent of change.**

1) From 150 to 450. ___ %

2) From 50 ft to 250 ft. ___ %

3) From $60 to $360. ___ %

4) From 60 cm to 180 cm. ___ %

5) From 15 to 45. ___ %

6) From 80 to 16. ___ %

7) From 120 to 360. ___ %

8) From 900 to 450. ___ %

9) From 1,000 to 200. ___ %

10) From 144 to 36. ___ %

✍ **Calculate each percent of change word problem.**

11) Bob got a raise, and his hourly wage increased from $42 to $63. What is the percent increase? ___ %

12) The price of a pair of shoes increases from $50 to $61. What is the percent increase? ___ %

13) At a coffee shop, the price of a cup of coffee increased from $4.80 to $5.76. What is the percent increase in the cost of the coffee? ___ %

14) 51 cm are cut from 85 cm board. What is the percent decrease in length? ___ %

15) In a class, the number of students has been increased from 54 to 81. What is the percent increase? ___ %

16) The price of gasoline rises from $24.40 to $30.50 in one month. By what percent did the gas price rise? ___ %

17) A shirt was originally priced at $38. It went on sale for $24.70. What was the percent that the shirt was discounted? ___ %

Simple Interest

🖎 **Determine the simple interest for these loans.**

1) $480 at 11% for 3 years. $ _____

2) $4,200 at 7% for 4 years. $ _____

3) $2,500 at 20% for 3 years. $ _____

4) $6,800 at 3.9% for 4 months. $ ____

5) $800 at 6% for 7 months. $ _____

6) $36,000 at 4.2% for 6 years. $ _____

7) $6,500 at 7% for 4 years. $ _____

8) $850 at 9.5% for 2 years. $ _____

9) $1,200 at 5.8% for 9 months. $ ____

10) $3,000 at 4.5% for 7 years. $ _____

🖎 **Calculate each simple interest word problem.**

11) A new car, valued at $22,000, depreciates at 8.5% per year. What is the value of the car one year after purchase? $_____

12) Sara puts $9,000 into an investment yielding 6% annual simple interest; she left the money in for three years. How much interest does Sara get at the end of those three years? $_____

13) A bank is offering 12% simple interest on a savings account. If you deposit $16,400, how much interest will you earn in two years? $_____

14) $720 interest is earned on a principal of $6,000 at a simple interest rate of 4% interest per year. For how many years was the principal invested? _____

15) In how many years will $2,200 yield an interest of $440 at 4% simple interest? _____

16) Jim invested $8,000 in a bond at a yearly rate of 4.5%. He earned $1,440 in interest. How long was the money invested? _____

Answers of Worksheets

Simplifying Ratios

1) 3 : 4

2) 1 : 10

3) 4 : 7

4) 1 : 3

5) 1 : 10

6) 1 : 8

7) 2 : 8

8) 2 : 5

9) 1 : 6

10) 7 : 9

11) 2 : 3

12) 7 : 2

13) 10 : 1

14) 3 : 4

15) 1 : 8

16) 5 : 7

17) 7 : 9

18) 2 : 1

19) 1 : 3

20) 7 : 1

21) 1 : 2

22) 5 : 4

23) 1 : 2

24) 1 : 30

25) $\frac{1}{2}$

26) $\frac{3}{5}$

27) $\frac{3}{7}$

28) $\frac{1}{3}$

29) $\frac{1}{3}$

30) $\frac{3}{14}$

31) $\frac{1}{2}$

32) $\frac{1}{5}$

33) $\frac{5}{12}$

34) $\frac{2}{9}$

35) $\frac{11}{13}$

36) $\frac{4}{9}$

37) $\frac{1}{12}$

38) $\frac{3}{11}$

39) $\frac{1}{15}$

40) $\frac{1}{4}$

41) $\frac{4}{3}$

42) $\frac{1}{5}$

43) $\frac{22}{41}$

44) $\frac{1}{9}$

45) $\frac{3}{5}$

Proportional Ratios

1) 18

2) 50

3) 9

4) 14

5) 14

6) 56

7) 100

8) 25

9) 70

10) 72

11) 200

12) 77

13) Yes

14) Yes

15) Yes

16) No

17) No

18) No

19) Yes

20) Yes

21) No

22) No

23) Yes

24) Yes

25) 40

26) 256

27) 7

28) 42

29) 63

30) 65

31) 20

32) 104

33) 55

34) 64

35) 126

36) 126

Similarity and ratios

1) 15

2) 5

3) 15

4) 13

5) 150 feet

6) 12.5 meters

7) 50 feet

8) 307.2 miles

Ratio and Rates Word Problems

1) 2 : 3

2) 315

3) The ratio for both classes is 7 to 4.   6) $51.75

4) Walmart is a better buy.   7) 56

5) 720, the rate is 30 per hour.   8) 15

Percentage Calculations

1) 1.8	11) 180	21) 8%
2) 6.4	12) 260	22) 32%
3) 2.88	13) 280	23) 2%
4) 5.12	14) 39.15	24) 80%
5) 31	15) 57.6	25) 16%
6) 19.6	16) 33	26) 7%
7) 3	17) 46.2	27) 14%
8) 21	18) 18.8	28) 42%
9) 40	19) 20%	29) 76%
10) 13.8	20) 50%	30) 40

Percent Problems

1) 20%	9) 15%	17) 63%
2) 50%	10) 65%	18) 580%
3) 5%	11) 25%	19) 62.5%
4) 12%	12) 20%	20) 15 ounces
5) 2.5%	13) 10%	21) 80
6) 120%	14) 225%	22) 80%
7) 25%	15) 450%	23) 30%
8) 80%	16) 30%	

Discount, Tax and Tip

1) $453.60	7) $315.00	13) $121.50
2) $291.20	8) $358.80	14) $47.04
3) $861.00	9) $43.50	15) $200.00
4) $16,368.80	10) $631.40	16) $112.50
5) $272.50	11) $51.75	17) $69.30
6) $641,340	12) $38.40	18) $714.00

Percent of Change

1) 200%	7) 200%	13) 20%
2) 400%	8) 50%	14) 60%
3) 500%	9) 80%	15) 50%
4) 200%	10) 75%	16) 25%
5) 200%	11) 50%	17) 35%
6) 80%	12) 22%	

Simple Interest

1) $158.40	7) $1,820.00	13) $3,936.00
2) $1,176.00	8) $161.50	14) 3 years
3) $1,500.00	9) $52.20	15) 5 years
4) $88.40	10) $945.00	16) 4 years
5) $28.00	11) $20,130.00	
6) $9,072.00	12) $1,620.00	

Chapter 4 :

Algebraic Expressions

Topics that you will practice in this chapter:

- ✓ Simplifying Variable Expressions
- ✓ Simplifying Polynomial Expressions
- ✓ Translate Phrases into an Algebraic Statement
- ✓ The Distributive Property
- ✓ Evaluating One Variable Expressions
- ✓ Evaluating Two Variables Expressions
- ✓ Combining like Terms

I want freedom for the full expression of my personality.

Mahatma Gandhi

Simplifying Variable Expressions

✎ **Simplify each expression.**

1) $3(x + 5) =$

2) $(-4)(7x - 5) =$

3) $11x + 5 - 6x =$

4) $-4 - 2x^2 - 6x^2 =$

5) $7 + 13x^2 + 3 =$

6) $3x^2 + 7x + 15x^2 =$

7) $3x^2 - 12x^2 + 4x =$

8) $4x^2 - 8x - 2x =$

9) $6x + 7(3 - 4x) =$

10) $8x + 4(15x - 3) =$

11) $6(-3x - 9) - 17 =$

12) $-11x^2 - (-5x) =$

13) $2x + 7 + 5 - 8x =$

14) $7 + 6x - 11 - 5x =$

15) $27x + 8 - 13 - 5x =$

16) $(-11)(-5x + 2) - 41x =$

17) $19x - 4(4 - 2x) =$

18) $16x + 3(3x + 6) + 10 =$

19) $5(-2x - 4) - 13x =$

20) $16x - 3x(x + 10) =$

21) $17x + 5x(2 - 4x) =$

22) $5x(-4x - 7) + 20x =$

23) $25x - 19 + 4x^2 =$

24) $6x(x - 11) + 25 =$

25) $4x - 5 + 15x + 3x^2 =$

26) $-7x^2 - 11x - 9x =$

27) $10x - 9x^2 - 3x^2 - 7 =$

28) $13 + 3x^2 - 9x^2 - 21x =$

29) $22x + 10x^2 - 15x + 17 =$

30) $4x^2 + 25x + 21x^2 =$

31) $29 - 12x^2 - 23x - 4x^2 =$

32) $22x - 19x - 9x^2 + 30 =$

Simplifying Polynomial Expressions

✎ Simplify each polynomial.

1) $(2x^3 + 8x^2) - (11x + 3x^2) =$ _____

2) $(2x^5 + 7x^3) - (5x^3 + 11x^2) =$ _____

3) $(41x^4 + 5x^2) - (4x^2 + 20x^4) =$ _____

4) $13x - 8x^2 + 4(4x^2 + 3x^3) =$ _____

5) $(4x^3 - 22) + 5(3x^2 - 6x^3) =$ _____

6) $(4x^3 - 3x) - 5(2x^3 + x^4) =$ _____

7) $5(5x - 2x^3) - 2(8x^3 + 5x^2) =$ _____

8) $(3x^2 - 10x) - (5x^3 + 14x^2) =$ _____

9) $5x^3 - (3x^4 + 5x) + 2x^2 =$ _____

10) $11x^4 - (3x^2 + 5x) + 7x =$ _____

11) $(6x^2 - 3x^4) - (10x^4 + 3x^2) =$ _____

12) $2x^2 - 7x^3 + 19x^4 - 22x^3 =$ _____

13) $10x^2 - x^4 + 4x^4 - 32x^3 =$ _____

14) $-5x^2 + 17x^3 - 8x^2 - 6x =$ _____

15) $x^4 - 11x^5 - 30x^4 + 5x^2 =$ _____

16) $21x^3 + 13x - 5x^2 - 11x^3 =$ _____

Translate Phrases into an Algebraic Statement

✍ **Write an algebraic expression for each phrase.**

1) 9 multiplied by x. _____

2) Subtract 11 from y. _____

3) 19 divided by x. _____

4) 38 decreased by y. _____

5) Add y to 40. _____

6) The square of 6. _____

7) x raised to the fifth power. _____

8) The sum of six and a number. _____

9) The difference between fifty–seven and y. _____

10) The quotient of nine and a number. _____

11) The quotient of the square of x and 25. _____

12) The difference between x and 6 is 19. _____

13) 10 times a reduced by the square of b. _____

14) Subtract the product of a and b from 41. _____

The Distributive Property

✎ Use the distributive property to simply each expression.

1) $4(1 + 2x) =$

2) $2(4 + 7x) =$

3) $3(4x - 4) =$

4) $(2x - 5)(-6) =$

5) $(-3)(x + 6) =$

6) $(4 + 3x)2 =$

7) $(-5)(8 - 3x) =$

8) $-(-5 - 7x) =$

9) $(-6x + 3)(-3) =$

10) $(-4)(x - 7) =$

11) $-(5 - 3x) =$

12) $3(9 + 4x) =$

13) $6(4 + 3x) =$

14) $(-5x + 3)2 =$

15) $(5 - 8x)(-3) =$

16) $(-12)(3x + 3) =$

17) $(5 - 3x)6 =$

18) $4(2 + 6x) =$

19) $8(7x - 3) =$

20) $(-2x + 3)4 =$

21) $(7 - 5x)(-9) =$

22) $(-10)(x - 8) =$

23) $(11 - 4x)3 =$

24) $(-6)(10x - 4) =$

25) $(3 - 9x)(-7) =$

26) $(-9)(x + 9) =$

27) $(-3 + 5x)(-7) =$

28) $(-5)(8 - 10x) =$

29) $12(4x - 8) =$

30) $(-10x + 13)(-3) =$

31) $(-8)(3x - 2) + 4(x + 5) =$

32) $(-8)(x + 4) - (6 + 5x) =$

Evaluating One Variable Expressions

✎ **Evaluate each expression using the value given.**

1) $8 - x, x = 5$

2) $x - 9, x = 5$

3) $5x + 4, x = 3$

4) $x - 13, x = -4$

5) $12 - x, x = 4$

6) $x + 2, x = 6$

7) $4x + 8, x = 3$

8) $x + (-7), x = -8$

9) $4x + 5, x = 2$

10) $3x + 9, x = -2$

11) $15 + 3x - 7, x = 2$

12) $17 - 3x, x = 3$

13) $8x - 9, x = 4$

14) $5x + 4, x = -3$

15) $10x + 5, x = 3$

16) $14 - 4x, x = -6$

17) $3(5x + 3), x = 9$

18) $4(-3x - 6), x = 3$

19) $7x - 2x + 12, x = 4$

20) $(5x + 6) \div 2, x = 8$

21) $(x + 18) \div 10, x = 12$

22) $5x - 12 + 3x, x = -3$

23) $(6 - 4x)(-3), x = -4$

24) $9x^2 + 3x - 6, x = 2$

25) $x^2 - 10x, x = -5$

26) $3x(7 - 2x), x = 2$

27) $12x + 6 - 2x^2, x = -4$

28) $(-3)(4x - 8 + 3x), x = 3$

29) $(-6) + \frac{x}{4} + 3x, x = 16$

30) $(-6) + \frac{x}{5}, x = 35$

31) $\left(-\frac{45}{x}\right) - 7 + 2x, x = 9$

32) $\left(-\frac{21}{x}\right) - 12 + 4x, x = 7$

Evaluating Two Variables Expressions

✎ Evaluate each expression using the values given.

1) $2x - 4y$,

    $x = 4, y = 1$

2) $3x + 5y$,

    $x = -2, y = 2$

3) $-7a + 4b$,

    $a = 2, b = 4$

4) $3x + 5 - y$,

    $x = 5, y = 6$

5) $3z + 12 - 2k$,

    $z = 5, k = 6$

6) $6(-x - 3y)$,

    $x = 5, y = -2$

7) $5a + 3b$,

    $a = 3, b = 4$

8) $7x \div 3y$,

    $x = 3, y = 7$

9) $2x + 15 + 5y$,

    $x = -3, y = 1$

10) $5a - (18 - b)$,

    $a = 2, b = 8$

11) $2z + 20 + 5k$,

    $z = -6, k = 5$

12) $xy + 10 + 4x$,

    $x = 3, y = 5$

13) $2x + 4y - 8 + 5$,

    $x = 5, y = 2$

14) $\left(-\frac{24}{x}\right) + 3 + 2y$,

    $x = 4, y = 6$

15) $(-3)(-3a - 3b)$,

    $a = 4, b = 5$

16) $12 + 4x - 7 - y$,

    $x = 3, y = 5$

17) $11x + 5 - 8y + 6$,

    $x = 5, y = 2$

18) $10 + 2(-4x - 5y)$,

    $x = 5, y = 4$

19) $5x + 13 + 6y$,

    $x = 5, y = 6$

20) $10a - (7a + 3b) - 11$,

    $a = 3, b = 8$

Combining like Terms

✍ **Simplify each expression.**

1) $11x + 3x + 6 =$

2) $8(2x - 6) =$

3) $18x - 7x + 11 =$

4) $(-4)(6x - 7) =$

5) $22x - 10x - 5 =$

6) $32x - 13 + 8x =$

7) $15 - (8x - 11) =$

8) $-24x + 17 - 11x =$

9) $12x - 8 - 6x + 9 =$

10) $21x + 5 - 36 + 12x =$

11) $28x + 3x - 11 =$

12) $(-3x + 4)5 =$

13) $2 + 4x + 9x - 8 =$

14) $6(2x - 5x) - 4 =$

15) $4(5x + 11) + 3x =$

16) $x - 14 - 11x =$

17) $5(10 + 9x) - 8x =$

18) $42x + 17 - 23x =$

19) $(-7x) + 19 + 20x =$

20) $(-7x) - 33 + 29x =$

21) $4(5x + 3) - 19x =$

22) $5(6 - 2x) - 15x =$

23) $-24x + (11 - 18x) =$

24) $(-9) - (6)(7x + 3) =$

25) $(-1)(8x - 10) - 21x =$

26) $-36x + 14 + 27x - 5x =$

27) $3(-13x + 6) - 17x =$

28) $-5x - 42 + 32x =$

29) $37x - 19x + 15 - 9x =$

30) $3(5x + 7x) - 31 =$

31) $14 - 6x - 15 - 9x =$

32) $-2(-5x - 7x) + 27x =$

Answers of Worksheets

Simplifying Variable Expressions

1) $3x + 15$
2) $-28x + 20$
3) $5x + 5$
4) $-8x^2 - 4$
5) $13x^2 + 10$
6) $18x^2 + 7x$
7) $-9x^2 + 4x$
8) $4x^2 - 10x$
9) $-22x + 21$
10) $68x - 12$
11) $-18x - 71$

12) $-11x^2 + 5x$
13) $-6x + 12$
14) $x - 4$
15) $22x - 5$
16) $14x - 22$
17) $27x - 16$
18) $25x + 28$
19) $-23x - 20$
20) $-3x^2 - 14x$
21) $-20x^2 + 27x$
22) $-20x^2 - 15x$

23) $4x^2 + 25x - 19$
24) $6x^2 - 66x + 25$
25) $3x^2 + 19x - 5$
26) $-7x^2 - 20x$
27) $-12x^2 + 10x - 7$
28) $-6x^2 - 21x + 13$
29) $10x^2 + 7x + 17$
30) $25x^2 + 25x$
31) $-16x^2 - 23x + 29$
32) $-9x^2 + 3x + 30$

Simplifying Polynomial Expressions

1) $2x^3 + 5x^2 - 11x$
2) $2x^5 + 2x^3 - 11x^2$
3) $21x^4 + x^2$
4) $12x^3 + 8x^2 + 13x$
5) $-26x^3 + 15x^2 - 22$
6) $-5x^4 - 6x^3 - 3x$
7) $-26x^3 - 10x^2 + 25x$
8) $-5x^3 - 11x^2 - 10x$

9) $-3x^4 + 5x^3 + 2x^2 - 5x$
10) $11x^4 - 3x^2 + 2x$
11) $-13x^4 + 3x^2$
12) $19x^4 - 29x^3 + 2x^2$
13) $3x^4 - 32x^3 + 10x^2$
14) $17x^3 - 13x^2 - 6x$
15) $-11x^5 - 29x^4 + 5x^2$
16) $10x^3 - 5x^2 + 13x$

Translate Phrases into an Algebraic Statement

1) $9x$
2) $y - 11$
3) $\frac{19}{x}$
4) $38 - y$

5) $y + 40$
6) 6^2
7) x^5
8) $6 + x$

9) $57 - y$
10) $\frac{9}{x}$
11) $\frac{x^2}{25}$

12) $x - 6 = 19$
13) $10a - b^2$
14) $41 - ab$

The Distributive Property

1) $8x + 4$
2) $14x + 8$
3) $12x - 12$

4) $-12x + 30$
5) $-3x - 18$
6) $6x + 8$

7) $15x - 40$
8) $7x + 5$
9) $18x - 9$

10) $-4x + 28$
11) $3x - 5$
12) $12x + 27$

13) $18x + 24$	18) $24x + 8$	23) $-12x + 33$	28) $50x - 40$
14) $-10x + 6$	19) $56x - 24$	24) $-60x + 24$	29) $48x - 96$
15) $24x - 15$	20) $-8x + 12$	25) $63x - 21$	30) $30x - 39$
16) $-36x - 36$	21) $45x - 63$	26) $-9x - 81$	31) $-20x + 36$
17) $-18x + 30$	22) $-10x + 80$	27) $-35x + 21$	32) $-13x - 38$

Evaluating One Variables

1) 3	9) 13	17) 144	25) 75
2) −4	10) 3	18) −60	26) 18
3) 19	11) 14	19) 32	27) −74
4) −17	12) 8	20) 23	28) −39
5) 8	13) 23	21) 3	29) 46
6) 8	14) −11	22) −36	30) 1
7) 20	15) 35	23) −66	31) 6
8) − 15	16) 38	24) 36	32) 13

Evaluating Two Variables

1) 4	6) 6	11) 33	16) 12
2) 4	7) 27	12) 37	17) 50
3) 2	8) 1	13) 15	18) −70
4) 14	9) 14	14) 9	19) 74
5) 15	10) 0	15) 81	20) −26

Combining like Terms

1) $14x + 6$	9) $6x + 1$	17) $37x + 50$	25) $-29x + 10$
2) $16x - 48$	10) $33x - 31$	18) $19x + 17$	26) $-14x + 14$
3) $11x + 11$	11) $31x - 11$	19) $13x + 19$	27) $-56x + 18$
4) $-24x + 28$	12) $-15x + 20$	20) $22x - 33$	28) $27x - 42$
5) $12x - 5$	13) $13x - 6$	21) $x + 12$	29) $9x + 15$
6) $40x - 13$	14) $-18x - 4$	22) $-25x + 30$	30) $36x - 31$
7) $-8x + 26$	15) $23x + 44$	23) $-42x + 11$	31) $-15x - 1$
8) $-35x + 17$	16) $-10x - 14$	24) $-42x - 27$	32) $51x$

Chapter 5 :

Exponents

Topics that you will practice in this chapter:

- ✓ Multiplication Property of Exponents
- ✓ Zero and Negative Exponents
- ✓ Division Property of Exponents
- ✓ Powers of Products and Quotients
- ✓ Negative Exponents and Negative Bases
- ✓ Scientific Notation

Love is anterior to life, posterior to death, initial of creation, and the exponent of breath.

Emily Dickinson

Multiplication Property of Exponents

✏️ Simplify and write the answer in exponential form.

1) $4 \times 4^5 =$

2) $8^4 \times 8 =$

3) $7^3 \times 7^3 =$

4) $9^2 \times 9^2 =$

5) $2^2 \times 2^4 \times 2 =$

6) $5 \times 5^3 \times 5^3 =$

7) $4^3 \times 4^2 \times 4 \times 4 =$

8) $5x \times x =$

9) $x^3 \times x^3 =$

10) $x^7 \times x^2 =$

11) $x^4 \times x^3 \times x^2 =$

12) $10x \times 3x =$

13) $4x^3 \times 4x^3 =$

14) $7x^3 \times x =$

15) $3x^2 \times 4x^2 \times x^2 =$

16) $5x^4 \times x^4 =$

17) $2x^8 \times 2x =$

18) $6x \times x^5 =$

19) $4x^2 \times 6x^6 =$

20) $5yx^3 \times 4x =$

21) $7x^3 \times y^5x^7 =$

22) $y^2x^3 \times y^5x^4 =$

23) $3x^5 \times 4x^3y^4 =$

24) $4x^4 \times 9x^2y^5 =$

25) $5x^3y^4 \times 6x^8y^2 =$

26) $8x^3y^6 \times 4xy^3 =$

27) $2xy^5 \times 6x^3y^3 =$

28) $4x^5y^2 \times 4x^2y^8 =$

29) $7x \times 3y^8x^2 \times y^5 =$

30) $x^3 \times 2y^3x^4 \times 2y =$

31) $3yx^4 \times 3y^4x \times 3xy^3 =$

32) $6y^3 \times 2y^2x^4 \times 10yx^5 =$

Zero and Negative Exponents

✎ **Evaluate the following expressions.**

1) $1^{-5} =$

2) $4^{-1} =$

3) $0^{10} =$

4) $1^{15} =$

5) $5^{-2} =$

6) $3^{-3} =$

7) $9^{-1} =$

8) $10^{-2} =$

9) $12^{-2} =$

10) $2^{-5} =$

11) $3^{-4} =$

12) $2^{-4} =$

13) $6^{-3} =$

14) $10^{-3} =$

15) $30^{-1} =$

16) $15^{-2} =$

17) $4^{-3} =$

18) $2^{-7} =$

19) $5^{-3} =$

20) $4^{-4} =$

21) $3^{-5} =$

22) $10^{-4} =$

23) $2^{-10} =$

24) $8^{-3} =$

25) $20^{-2} =$

26) $14^{-2} =$

27) $9^{-3} =$

28) $100^{-2} =$

29) $5^{-4} =$

30) $4^{-6} =$

31) $\left(\frac{1}{4}\right)^{-3}$

32) $\left(\frac{1}{6}\right)^{-2} =$

33) $\left(\frac{1}{7}\right)^{-2} =$

34) $\left(\frac{2}{3}\right)^{-3} =$

35) $\left(\frac{1}{13}\right)^{-2} =$

36) $\left(\frac{7}{12}\right)^{-2} =$

37) $\left(\frac{1}{6}\right)^{-3} =$

38) $\left(\frac{1}{300}\right)^{-2} =$

39) $\left(\frac{2}{9}\right)^{-2} =$

40) $\left(\frac{7}{5}\right)^{-1} =$

41) $\left(\frac{13}{23}\right)^{0} =$

42) $\left(\frac{1}{4}\right)^{-5} =$

Division Property of Exponents

✍ **Simplify.**

1) $\dfrac{5^6}{5^7} =$

2) $\dfrac{8^8}{8^6} =$

3) $\dfrac{4^5}{4} =$

4) $\dfrac{3}{3^5} =$

5) $\dfrac{x}{x^6} =$

6) $\dfrac{3 \times 3^2}{3^2 \times 3^5} =$

7) $\dfrac{9^4}{9^2} =$

8) $\dfrac{10 \times 10^9}{10^2 \times 10^7} =$

9) $\dfrac{7^5 \times 7^7}{7^4 \times 7^8} =$

10) $\dfrac{15x}{30x^6} =$

11) $\dfrac{3x^9}{4x^4} =$

12) $\dfrac{15x^8}{10x^9} =$

13) $\dfrac{42x^5}{6y^9} =$

14) $\dfrac{36y^8}{4x^4y^5} =$

15) $\dfrac{2x^7}{9x} =$

16) $\dfrac{49x^8y^6}{7x^9} =$

17) $\dfrac{48x^2}{24x^6y^{12}} =$

18) $\dfrac{30yx^5}{6yx^7} =$

19) $\dfrac{19x^7y}{38x^{12}y^4} =$

20) $\dfrac{9x^8}{63x^8} =$

21) $\dfrac{9x^{-9}}{4x^{-3}} =$

Powers of Products and Quotients

✎ **Simplify.**

1) $(4^3)^2 =$

2) $(2^3)^4 =$

3) $(2 \times 2^3)^2 =$

4) $(5 \times 5^5)^6 =$

5) $(19^4 \times 19^2)^3 =$

6) $(2^3 \times 2^4)^4 =$

7) $(5 \times 5^2)^2 =$

8) $(4^4)^4 =$

9) $(8x^5)^2 =$

10) $(3x^2y^4)^4 =$

11) $(7x^5y^2)^2 =$

12) $(5x^4y^4)^3 =$

13) $(2x^3y^3)^5 =$

14) $(10x^3y^4)^3 =$

15) $(13y^3y)^2 =$

16) $(5x^6x^4)^2 =$

17) $(6x^7y^6)^3 =$

18) $(12x^5x^7)^2 =$

19) $(2x^4 \times 2x)^4 =$

20) $(2x^4y^3)^5 =$

21) $(15x^7y^2)^2 =$

22) $(8x^3y^5)^3 =$

23) $(3x \times 2y^2)^4 =$

24) $\left(\frac{4x}{x^5}\right)^2 =$

25) $\left(\frac{x^4y^5}{x^3y^5}\right)^9 =$

26) $\left(\frac{36xy}{6x^5}\right)^3 =$

27) $\left(\frac{x^7}{x^8y^2}\right)^6 =$

28) $\left(\frac{xy^4}{x^3y^6}\right)^{-3} =$

29) $\left(\frac{5xy^8}{x^3}\right)^2 =$

30) $\left(\frac{xy^6}{2xy^3}\right)^{-4} =$

Negative Exponents and Negative Bases

✎ **Simplify.**

1) $-9^{-1} =$

2) $-9^{-2} =$

3) $-2^{-5} =$

4) $-x^{-7} =$

5) $11x^{-1} =$

6) $-8x^{-3} =$

7) $-12x^{-5} =$

8) $-9x^{-8}y^{-6} =$

9) $32x^{-5}y^{-1} =$

10) $10a^{-9}b^{-3} =$

11) $-17x^4y^{-6} =$

12) $-\dfrac{25}{x^{-5}} =$

13) $-\dfrac{13x}{a^{-7}} =$

14) $\left(-\dfrac{1}{3}\right)^{-4} =$

15) $\left(-\dfrac{3}{4}\right)^{-2} =$

16) $-\dfrac{14}{a^{-6}b^{-3}} =$

17) $-\dfrac{7x}{x^{-8}} =$

18) $-\dfrac{a^{-9}}{b^{-5}} =$

19) $-\dfrac{11}{x^{-5}} =$

20) $\dfrac{8b}{-16c^{-6}} =$

21) $\dfrac{12ab}{a^{-4}b^{-3}} =$

22) $-\dfrac{8n^{-4}}{32p^{-7}} =$

23) $\dfrac{16ab^{-6}}{-6c^{-5}} =$

24) $\left(\dfrac{10a}{5c}\right)^{-4} =$

25) $\left(-\dfrac{12x}{4yz}\right)^{-3} =$

26) $\dfrac{8ab^{-7}}{-5c^{-3}} =$

27) $\left(-\dfrac{x^4}{x^5}\right)^{-5} =$

28) $\left(-\dfrac{x^{-2}}{7x^3}\right)^{-2} =$

29) $\left(-\dfrac{x^{-4}}{x^2}\right)^{-6} =$

Scientific Notation

✎ **Write each number in scientific notation.**

1) $0.223 =$

2) $0.09 =$

3) $4.5 =$

4) $900 =$

5) $2,000 =$

6) $0.006 =$

7) $33 =$

8) $9,400 =$

9) $1,470 =$

10) $52,000 =$

11) $8,000,000 =$

12) $0.00009 =$

13) $2,158,000 =$

14) $0.0039 =$

15) $0.000075 =$

16) $4,300,000 =$

17) $130,000 =$

18) $4,000,000,000 =$

19) $0.00009 =$

20) $0.0039 =$

✎ **Write each number in standard notation.**

21) $4 \times 10^{-1} =$

22) $1.2 \times 10^{-3} =$

23) $2.7 \times 10^5 =$

24) $6 \times 10^{-4} =$

25) $3.6 \times 10^{-3} =$

26) $5.5 \times 10^5 =$

27) $3.2 \times 10^4 =$

28) $3.88 \times 10^6 =$

29) $7 \times 10^{-6} =$

30) $4.2 \times 10^{-7} =$

Answers of Worksheets

Multiplication Property of Exponents

1) 4^6
2) 8^5
3) 7^6
4) 9^4
5) 2^7
6) 5^7
7) 4^7
8) $5x^2$

9) x^6
10) x^9
11) x^9
12) $30x^2$
13) $16x^6$
14) $7x^4$
15) $12x^6$
16) $5x^8$

17) $4x^9$
18) $6x^6$
19) $24x^8$
20) $20x^4y$
21) $7x^{10}y^5$
22) x^7y^7
23) $12x^8y^4$
24) $36x^6y^5$

25) $30x^{11}y^6$
26) $32x^4y^9$
27) $12x^4y^8$
28) $16x^7y^{10}$
29) $21x^3y^{13}$
30) $4x^7y^4$
31) $27x^6y^8$
32) $120x^9y^6$

Zero and Negative Exponents

1) 1
2) $\frac{1}{4}$
3) 0
4) 1
5) $\frac{1}{25}$
6) $\frac{1}{27}$
7) $\frac{1}{9}$
8) $\frac{1}{100}$
9) $\frac{1}{144}$
10) $\frac{1}{32}$

11) $\frac{1}{81}$
12) $\frac{1}{16}$
13) $\frac{1}{216}$
14) $\frac{1}{1,000}$
15) $\frac{1}{30}$
16) $\frac{1}{225}$
17) $\frac{1}{64}$
18) $\frac{1}{128}$
19) $\frac{1}{125}$
20) $\frac{1}{256}$

21) $\frac{1}{243}$
22) $\frac{1}{10,000}$
23) $\frac{1}{1,024}$
24) $\frac{1}{512}$
25) $\frac{1}{400}$
26) $\frac{1}{196}$
27) $\frac{1}{729}$
28) $\frac{1}{10,000}$
29) $\frac{1}{625}$
30) $\frac{1}{4,096}$

31) 64
32) 36
33) 49
34) $\frac{27}{8}$
35) 169
36) $\frac{144}{49}$
37) 216
38) $90,000$
39) $\frac{81}{4}$
40) $\frac{5}{7}$
41) 1
42) $1,024$

Division Property of Exponents

1) $\frac{1}{5}$
2) 8^2
3) 4^4
4) $\frac{1}{3^4}$

5) $\frac{1}{x^5}$
6) $\frac{1}{3^4}$
7) 9^2
8) 10
9) 1

10) $\frac{1}{2x^5}$
11) $\frac{3x^5}{4}$
12) $\frac{3}{2x}$
13) $\frac{7x^5}{y^9}$

14) $\frac{9y^3}{x^4}$
15) $\frac{2x^6}{9}$
16) $\frac{7y^6}{x}$
17) $\frac{2}{x^4y^{12}}$

18) $\frac{5}{x^2}$ 19) $\frac{1}{2x^5y^3}$ 20) $\frac{1}{7}$ 21) $\frac{9}{4x^6}$

Powers of Products and Quotients

1) 4^6

2) 2^{12}

3) 2^8

4) 5^{36}

5) 19^{18}

6) 2^{28}

7) 5^6

8) 4^{16}

9) $64x^{10}$

10) $81x^8y^{16}$

11) $49x^{10}y^4$

12) $125x^{12}y^{12}$

13) $32x^{15}y^{15}$

14) $1{,}000x^9y^{12}$

15) $169y^8$

16) $25x^{20}$

17) $216x^{21}y^{18}$

18) $144x^{24}$

19) $256x^{20}$

20) $32x^{20}y^{15}$

21) $225x^{14}y^4$

22) $512x^9y^{15}$

23) $1{,}296x^4y^8$

24) $\frac{16}{x^8}$

25) x^9

26) $\frac{216y^3}{x^{12}}$

27) $\frac{1}{x^6y^{12}}$

28) x^6y^6

29) $\frac{25y^{16}}{x^4}$

30) $\frac{16}{y^{12}}$

Negative Exponents and Negative Bases

1) $-\frac{1}{9}$

2) $-\frac{1}{81}$

3) $-\frac{1}{32}$

4) $-\frac{1}{x^7}$

5) $\frac{11}{x}$

6) $-\frac{8}{x^3}$

7) $-\frac{12}{x^5}$

8) $-\frac{9}{x^8y^6}$

9) $\frac{32}{x^5y}$

10) $\frac{10}{a^9b^3}$

11) $-\frac{17x^4}{y^6}$

12) $-25x^5$

13) $-13xa^7$

14) 81

15) $\frac{16}{9}$

16) $-14a^6b^3$

17) $-7x^9$

18) $-\frac{b^5}{a^9}$

19) $-11x^5$

20) $-\frac{bc^6}{2}$

21) $12a^5b^4$

22) $-\frac{p^7}{4n^4}$

23) $-\frac{8ac^5}{3b^6}$

24) $\frac{c^4}{16a^4}$

25) $\frac{y^3z^3}{27x^3}$

26) $-\frac{8ac^3}{5b^7}$

27) $-x^5$

28) $49x^{10}$

29) x^{36}

Scientific Notation

1) 2.23×10^{-1}

2) 9×10^{-2}

3) 4.5×10^0

4) 9×10^2

5) 2×10^3

6) 6×10^{-3}

7) 3.3×10^1

8) 9.4×10^3

9) 1.47×10^3

10) 5.2×10^4

11) 8×10^6

12) 9×10^{-5}

13) 2.158×10^6

14) 3.9×10^{-3}

15) 7.5×10^{-5}

16) 4.3×10^6

17) 1.3×10^5

18) 4×10^9

19) 9×10^{-5}

20) 3.9×10^{-3}

21) 0.4

22) 0.0012

23) $270,000$

24) 0.0006

25) 0.0036

26) $550,000$

27) $32,000$

28) $3,880,000$

29) 0.000007

30) 0.00000042

Chapter 6 :

Radicals Expressions

Topics that you'll practice in this chapter:

✓ Square Roots

✓ Simplifying Radical Expressions

✓ Adding and Subtracting Radical Expressions

✓ Simplifying Radical Expressions Involving Fractions

✓ Multiplying Radical Expressions

"To be radical is to grasp things by the root."
— Karl Marx,

Square Roots

✎ **Find the value each square root.**

1) $\sqrt{16} =$ ___

2) $\sqrt{25} =$ ___

3) $\sqrt{1} =$ ___

4) $\sqrt{64} =$ ___

5) $\sqrt{0} =$ ___

6) $\sqrt{196} =$ ___

7) $\sqrt{4} =$ ___

8) $\sqrt{256} =$ ___

9) $\sqrt{36} =$ ___

10) $\sqrt{289} =$ ___

11) $\sqrt{169} =$ ___

12) $\sqrt{144} =$ ___

13) $\sqrt{100} =$ ___

14) $\sqrt{1,600} =$ ___

15) $\sqrt{2,500} =$ ___

16) $\sqrt{324} =$ ___

17) $\sqrt{529} =$ ___

18) $\sqrt{20} =$ ___

19) $\sqrt{625} =$ ___

20) $\sqrt{18} =$ ___

21) $\sqrt{50} =$ ___

22) $\sqrt{1,024} =$ ___

23) $\sqrt{160} =$ ___

24) $\sqrt{32} =$ ___

✎ **Evaluate.**

25) $\sqrt{4} \times \sqrt{25} =$ _____

26) $\sqrt{36} \times \sqrt{49} =$ _____

27) $\sqrt{6} \times \sqrt{6} =$ _____

28) $\sqrt{13} \times \sqrt{13} =$ _____

29) $2\sqrt{5} \times 3\sqrt{5} =$ _____

30) $\sqrt{12} \times \sqrt{3} =$ _____

31) $\sqrt{13} + \sqrt{13} =$ _____

32) $\sqrt{10} + 2\sqrt{10} =$ _____

33) $12\sqrt{7} - 10\sqrt{7} =$ _____

34) $4\sqrt{10} \times 2\sqrt{10} =$ _____

35) $5\sqrt{3} \times 8\sqrt{3} =$ _____

36) $6\sqrt{3} - \sqrt{12} =$ _____

Simplifying Radical Expressions

✎ **Simplify.**

1) $\sqrt{13x^2} =$

2) $\sqrt{75x^2} =$

3) $\sqrt[3]{27a} =$

4) $\sqrt{64x^5} =$

5) $\sqrt{216a} =$

6) $\sqrt[3]{63w^3} =$

7) $\sqrt{192x} =$

8) $\sqrt{125v} =$

9) $\sqrt[3]{128x^2} =$

10) $\sqrt{100x^9} =$

11) $\sqrt{16x^4} =$

12) $\sqrt[3]{500a^5} =$

13) $\sqrt{242} =$

14) $\sqrt{392p^3} =$

15) $\sqrt{8m^6} =$

16) $\sqrt{198x^3y^3} =$

17) $\sqrt{121x^5y^5} =$

18) $\sqrt{16a^6b^3} =$

19) $\sqrt{90x^5y^7} =$

20) $\sqrt[3]{64y^2x^6} =$

21) $10\sqrt{16x^4} =$

22) $6\sqrt{81x^2} =$

23) $\sqrt[3]{56x^2y^6} =$

24) $\sqrt[3]{1,000x^5y^7} =$

25) $8\sqrt{50a} =$

26) $\sqrt[4]{625x^8y} =$

27) $\sqrt{24x^4y^5r^3} =$

28) $5\sqrt{36x^4y^5z^8} =$

29) $3\sqrt[3]{343x^9y^7} =$

30) $5\sqrt{81a^5b^2c^9} =$

31) $\sqrt[4]{625x^8y^{16}} =$

Adding and Subtracting Radical Expressions

✎ Simplify.

1) $\sqrt{2} + \sqrt{8} =$

2) $3\sqrt{50} + 4\sqrt{2} =$

3) $2\sqrt{12} - 4\sqrt{3} =$

4) $5\sqrt{32} - 5\sqrt{2} =$

5) $3\sqrt{75} - 5\sqrt{3} =$

6) $-\sqrt{72} - 4\sqrt{2} =$

7) $-7\sqrt{16} - 4\sqrt{25} =$

8) $8\sqrt{24} + 2\sqrt{6} =$

9) $10\sqrt{49} - 7\sqrt{100} =$

10) $-7\sqrt{5} + 9\sqrt{45} =$

11) $-15\sqrt{12} + 14\sqrt{48} =$

12) $20\sqrt{4} - 2\sqrt{25} =$

13) $-2\sqrt{20} + 7\sqrt{5} =$

14) $8\sqrt{7} - 2\sqrt{63} =$

15) $5\sqrt{44} + 3\sqrt{11} =$

16) $3\sqrt{27} - 5\sqrt{48} =$

17) $\sqrt{144} - \sqrt{81} =$

18) $3\sqrt{20} - 6\sqrt{5} =$

19) $-2\sqrt{7} + 8\sqrt{28} =$

20) $3\sqrt{75} - 2\sqrt{3} =$

21) $5\sqrt{27} - 3\sqrt{3} =$

22) $-7\sqrt{30} + 6\sqrt{120} =$

23) $-7\sqrt{24} - 2\sqrt{6} =$

24) $-\sqrt{32x} + 4\sqrt{2x} =$

25) $\sqrt{7y^2} + y\sqrt{112} =$

26) $\sqrt{45mn^2} + 2n\sqrt{5m} =$

27) $-4\sqrt{12a} - 4\sqrt{3a} =$

28) $-5\sqrt{15ab} - 2\sqrt{60ab} =$

29) $\sqrt{45x^2y} + x\sqrt{20y} =$

30) $2\sqrt{7a} + 4\sqrt{63a} =$

Multiplying Radical Expressions

✍ **Simplify.**

1) $\sqrt{5} \times \sqrt{5} =$

2) $\sqrt{5} \times \sqrt{10} =$

3) $\sqrt{3} \times \sqrt{12} =$

4) $\sqrt{49} \times \sqrt{47} =$

5) $\sqrt{7} \times -2\sqrt{28} =$

6) $3\sqrt{15} \times \sqrt{5} =$

7) $4\sqrt{72} \times \sqrt{2} =$

8) $\sqrt{5} \times -\sqrt{49} =$

9) $\sqrt{55} \times \sqrt{11} =$

10) $7\sqrt{42} \times 2\sqrt{216} =$

11) $\sqrt{45}(5 + \sqrt{5}) =$

12) $\sqrt{13x^2} \times \sqrt{13x^3} =$

13) $-2\sqrt{27} \times \sqrt{3} =$

14) $2\sqrt{13x^4} \times \sqrt{13x^4} =$

15) $\sqrt{14x^3} \times \sqrt{7x^2} =$

16) $-8\sqrt{5x} \times \sqrt{7x^5} =$

17) $-2\sqrt{16x^5} \times 4\sqrt{8x^3} =$

18) $-4\sqrt{32}(8 + \sqrt{32}) =$

19) $\sqrt{32x}(10 - \sqrt{2x}) =$

20) $\sqrt{2x}(8\sqrt{x^5} + \sqrt{8}) =$

21) $\sqrt{20r}(5 + \sqrt{5}) =$

22) $-4\sqrt{7x} \times 3\sqrt{14x^5} =$

23) $-2\sqrt{12x} \times 3\sqrt{2x}$

24) $-\sqrt{7v^3}(-3\sqrt{42v}) =$

25) $(\sqrt{11} - 5)(\sqrt{11} + 5) =$

26) $(-3\sqrt{5} + 3)(\sqrt{5} - 4) =$

27) $(4 - 6\sqrt{3})(-6 + \sqrt{3}) =$

28) $(8 - 3\sqrt{5})(7 - \sqrt{5}) =$

29) $(-1 - \sqrt{3x})(4 + \sqrt{3x}) =$

30) $(-5 + 2\sqrt{7r})(-5 + \sqrt{7r}) =$

31) $(-\sqrt{7n} + 1)(-\sqrt{7} - 5) =$

32) $(-3 + \sqrt{3})(5 - 2\sqrt{3x}) =$

Simplifying Radical Expressions Involving Fractions

✎ **Simplify.**

1) $\dfrac{\sqrt{5}}{\sqrt{3}} =$

2) $\dfrac{\sqrt{18}}{\sqrt{45}} =$

3) $\dfrac{\sqrt{10}}{5\sqrt{2}} =$

4) $\dfrac{13}{\sqrt{3}} =$

5) $\dfrac{12\sqrt{5r}}{\sqrt{m^5}} =$

6) $\dfrac{11\sqrt{2}}{\sqrt{k}} =$

7) $\dfrac{6\sqrt{20x^3}}{\sqrt{16x}} =$

8) $\dfrac{\sqrt{14x^3y^4}}{\sqrt{7x^4y^3}} =$

9) $\dfrac{1}{1-\sqrt{5}} =$

10) $\dfrac{1-8\sqrt{a}}{\sqrt{11a}} =$

11) $\dfrac{\sqrt{a}}{\sqrt{a}+\sqrt{b}} =$

12) $\dfrac{1-\sqrt{5}}{2-\sqrt{6}} =$

13) $\dfrac{4+\sqrt{7}}{3-\sqrt{8}} =$

14) $\dfrac{5}{-3-3\sqrt{3}} =$

15) $\dfrac{7}{2-\sqrt{5}} =$

16) $\dfrac{\sqrt{7}-\sqrt{3}}{\sqrt{3}-\sqrt{7}} =$

17) $\dfrac{\sqrt{5}+\sqrt{7}}{\sqrt{7}-\sqrt{5}} =$

18) $\dfrac{2\sqrt{2}-\sqrt{3}}{3\sqrt{2}+\sqrt{5}} =$

19) $\dfrac{\sqrt{11}+5\sqrt{3}}{4-\sqrt{11}} =$

20) $\dfrac{\sqrt{5}+\sqrt{3}}{2-\sqrt{3}} =$

21) $\dfrac{\sqrt{32a^7b^4}}{\sqrt{2ab^3}} =$

22) $\dfrac{10\sqrt{21x^5}}{5\sqrt{x^3}} =$

Answers of Worksheets

Square Roots

1) 4
2) 5
3) 1
4) 8
5) 0
6) 14
7) 2
8) 16
9) 6
10) 17
11) 13
12) 12
13) 10
14) 40
15) 50
16) 18
17) 23
18) $2\sqrt{5}$
19) 25
20) $3\sqrt{2}$
21) $5\sqrt{2}$
22) 32
23) $4\sqrt{10}$
24) $4\sqrt{2}$
25) 10
26) 42
27) 6
28) 13
29) 30
30) 6
31) $2\sqrt{13}$
32) $3\sqrt{10}$
33) $2\sqrt{7}$
34) 80
35) 120
36) $4\sqrt{3}$

Simplifying radical expressions

1) $x\sqrt{13}$
2) $5x\sqrt{3}$
3) $3\sqrt[3]{a}$
4) $8x^2\sqrt{x}$
5) $6\sqrt{6a}$
6) $w\sqrt[3]{63}$
7) $8\sqrt{3x}$
8) $5\sqrt{5v}$
9) $4\sqrt[3]{2x^2}$
10) $10x^4\sqrt{x}$
11) $4x^2$
12) $5a\sqrt[3]{4a^2}$
13) $11\sqrt{2}$
14) $14p\sqrt{2p}$
15) $2m^3\sqrt{2}$
16) $3x.y\sqrt{22xy}$
17) $11x^2y^2\sqrt{xy}$
18) $4a^3b\sqrt{b}$
19) $3x^2y^3\sqrt{10xy}$
20) $4x^2\sqrt[3]{y^2}$
21) $40x^2$
22) $54x$
23) $2y^2\sqrt[3]{7x^2}$
24) $10xy^2\sqrt[3]{x^2y}$
25) $40\sqrt{2a}$
26) $5x^2\sqrt[4]{y}$
27) $2x^2y^2r\sqrt{6yr}$
28) $30x^2y^2z^4\sqrt{y}$
29) $21x^3y^2\sqrt[3]{y}$
30) $45a^2bc^4\sqrt{ac}$
31) $5x^2y^4$

Adding and subtracting radical expressions

1) $3\sqrt{2}$
2) $19\sqrt{2}$
3) 0
4) $15\sqrt{2}$
5) $10\sqrt{3}$
6) $-10\sqrt{2}$
7) -48
8) $18\sqrt{6}$
9) 0
10) $20\sqrt{5}$
11) $26\sqrt{3}$
12) 30
13) $3\sqrt{5}$
14) $2\sqrt{7}$
15) $13\sqrt{11}$

16) $-11\sqrt{3}$

17) 3

18) 0

19) $14\sqrt{7}$

20) $13\sqrt{3}$

21) $12\sqrt{3}$

22) $5\sqrt{30}$

23) $-16\sqrt{6}$

24) 0

25) $5y\sqrt{7}$

26) $5n\sqrt{5m}$

27) $-12\sqrt{3a}$

28) $-9\sqrt{15ab}$

29) $5x\sqrt{5y}$

30) $14\sqrt{7a}$

Multiplying radical expressions

1) 5

2) $5\sqrt{2}$

3) 6

4) $7\sqrt{47}$

5) -28

6) $15\sqrt{3}$

7) 48

8) $-5\sqrt{7}$

9) $11\sqrt{5}$

10) $504\sqrt{7}$

11) $15\sqrt{5} + 15$

12) $13x^2\sqrt{x}$

13) -18

14) $26x^4$

15) $7x^2\sqrt{2x}$

16) $-8x^3\sqrt{35}$

17) $-64x^4\sqrt{2}$

18) $-128\sqrt{2} - 128$

19) $40\sqrt{2x} - 8x$

20) $8x^3\sqrt{2} + 4\sqrt{x}$

21) $10\sqrt{5r} + 10\sqrt{r}$

22) $-84x^3\sqrt{2}$

23) $-12\sqrt{6}x$

24) $21v^2\sqrt{6}$

25) -14

26) $15\sqrt{5} - 27$

27) $40\sqrt{3} - 42$

28) $71 - 29\sqrt{5}$

29) $-3x - 5\sqrt{3x} - 4$

30) $14r - 15\sqrt{7r} + 25$

31) $7\sqrt{n} + 5\sqrt{7n} - \sqrt{7} - 5$

32) $-15 + 6\sqrt{3x} + 5\sqrt{3} - 6\sqrt{x}$

Simplifying radical expressions involving fractions

1) $\frac{\sqrt{15}}{3}$

2) $\frac{9\sqrt{10}}{45} = \frac{\sqrt{10}}{5}$

3) $\frac{\sqrt{20}}{10} = \frac{\sqrt{5}}{5}$

4) $\frac{13\sqrt{3}}{3}$

5) $\frac{12\sqrt{5mr}}{m^3}$

6) $\frac{11\sqrt{2k}}{k}$

7) $3x\sqrt{5}$

8) $\frac{\sqrt{2x}}{xy}$

9) $\dfrac{-1-\sqrt{5}}{4}$

10) $\dfrac{\sqrt{11a}-8a\sqrt{11}}{11a}$

11) $\dfrac{a-\sqrt{ab}}{a-b}$

12) $\dfrac{\sqrt{30}+2\sqrt{5}-\sqrt{6}-2}{2}$

13) $12 + 8\sqrt{2} + 3\sqrt{7} + 2\sqrt{14}$

14) $-\dfrac{5(\sqrt{3}-1)}{6}$

15) $-14 - 7\sqrt{5}$

16) -1

17) $6 + \sqrt{35}$

18) $\dfrac{12 - 2\sqrt{10} - 3\sqrt{6} + \sqrt{15}}{13}$

19) $\dfrac{4\sqrt{11}+11+20\sqrt{3}+5\sqrt{33}}{5}$

20) $2\sqrt{5} + 3 + \sqrt{15} + 2\sqrt{3}$

21) $4a^3\sqrt{b}$

22) $2x\sqrt{21}$

Chapter 7 :

Linear Functions

Topics that you'll practice in this chapter:

- ✓ Finding Slope,
- ✓ Graphing Linear Equations,
- ✓ Graphing Linear Inequalities,
- ✓ Writing Linear Equations,
- ✓ Graphing Horizontal and Vertical lines
- ✓ Finding Rate of Change,
- ✓ Find the x–intercept and y–intercept,
- ✓ Slope-Intercept Form Equations,
- ✓ Point-Slope Form Equations,
- ✓ Equation of parallel or perpendicular lines,
- ✓ Graphing Lines of Equations,
- ✓ Graphing Absolute Value Equations

Life is not linear; you have ups and downs. It's how you deal with the troughs that defines you.
Michael Lee-Chin

Finding Slope

✎ Find the slope of each line.

1) $y = x + 8$

2) $y = -3x + 5$

3) $y = 2x + 12$

4) $y = -4x + 19$

5) $y = 11 + 6x$

6) $y = 7 - 5x$

7) $y = 8x + 19$

8) $y = -9x + 20$

9) $y = -7x + 4$

10) $y = 3x - 8$

11) $y = \frac{1}{3}x + 8$

12) $y = -\frac{4}{5}x + 9$

13) $-3x + 6y = 30$

14) $4x + 4y = 16$

15) $3y - x = 10$

16) $8y - x = 5$

✎ Find the slope of the line through each pair of points.

17) $(2, 3), (7, 10)$

18) $(-3, 5), (2, 15)$

19) $(5, -3), (1, 9)$

20) $(-5, -5), (10, 25)$

21) $(22, 3), (7, 18)$

22) $(-16, 8), (-7, 26)$

23) $(25, 11), (29, 19)$

24) $(26, -19), (14, 17)$

25) $(22, -13), (20, -11)$

26) $(19, 7), (15, -3)$

27) $(5, 7), (11, 19)$

28) $(52, -62), (40, 70)$

Graphing Linear Equations

 Sketch the graph of each line.

1) $y = x - 2$

2) $y = -3x + 2$

3) $x + y = 0$

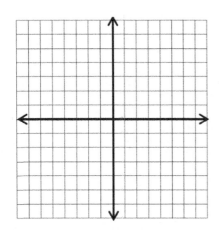   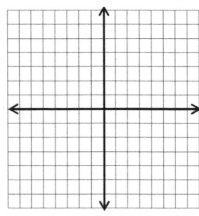   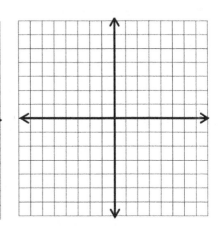

4) $x + y = -3$

5) $2x + 3y = -4$

6) $y - 3x + 6 = 0$

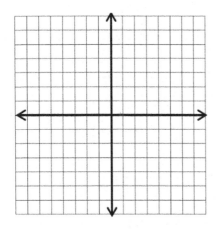   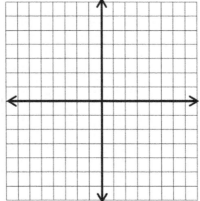   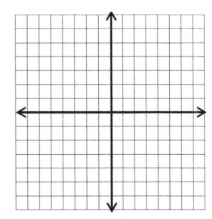

Graphing Linear Inequalities

✏️ **Sketch the graph of each linear inequality.**

1) $y > 4x - 5$ 2) $y < 2x + 4$ 3) $y \leq -5x - 2$

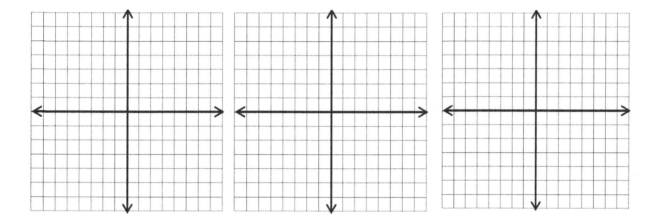

4) $4y \geq 12 + 4x$ 5) $-12y < 3x - 24$ 6) $5y \geq -15x + 10$

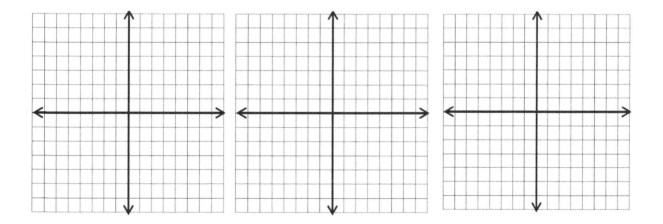

Writing Linear Equations

✍ **Write the equation of the line through the given points.**

1) Through: $(2, -5), (3, 9)$

2) Through: $(-6, 3), (3, 12)$

3) Through: $(10, 7), (5, 27)$

4) Through: $(15, 11), (3, -1)$

5) Through: $(24, 17), (12, -7)$

6) Through: $(8, 29), (4, -7)$

7) Through: $(20, -16), (12, 0)$

8) Through: $(-3, 10), (2, -5)$

9) Through: $(-6, 17), (4, -3)$

10) Through: $(-8, 22), (5, -4)$

11) Through: $(9, 27), (3, -3)$

12) Through: $(11, 32), (9, 4)$

13) Through: $(-3, 13), (-4, 0)$

14) Through: $(-5, 5), (5, 15)$

15) Through: $(18, -32), (11, 3)$

16) Through: $(-4, 25), (4, -15)$

✍ **Find the answer for each problem.**

17) What is the equation of a line with slope 6 and intercept 12?
_____

18) What is the equation of a line with slope -11 and intercept -4?
_____

19) What is the equation of a line with slope -3 and passes through point $(5, 2)$? _____

20) What is the equation of a line with slope -5 and passes through point $(-2, -1)$? _____

21) The slope of a line is -10 and it passes through point $(-3, 0)$. What is the equation of the line? _____

22) The slope of a line is 8 and it passes through point $(0, 7)$. What is the equation of the line? _____

✎ **Find the value of** b**: The line that passes through each pair of points**

has the given slope.

1) $(5, -4), (2, b), m = 1$

3) $(-4, b), (4, 8), m = \frac{1}{2}$

2) $(b, -4), (-4, 1), m = -\frac{1}{3}$

4) $(0, 3), (b, 8), m = 1\frac{2}{3}$

✎ **Write the slope intercept form of the equation of each line.**

1)

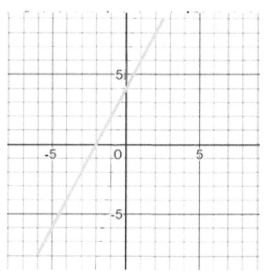

2)

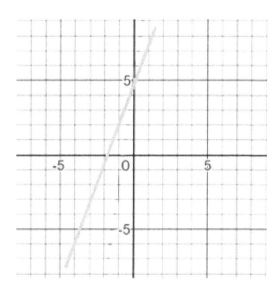

3)

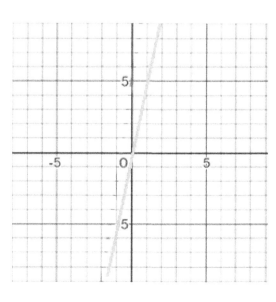

4)

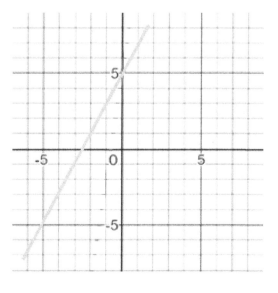

Graphing Horizontal and Vertical Lines

✍ **Sketch the graph of each line.**

1) $y = 3$

2) $y = -1$

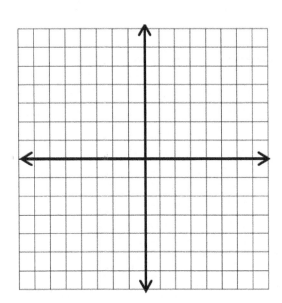
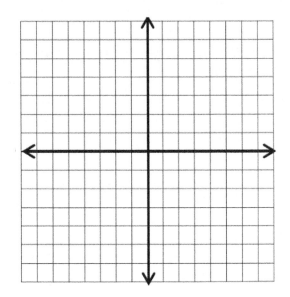

3) $x = 0$

4) $x = 3$

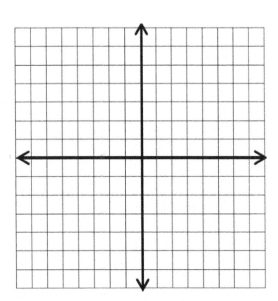
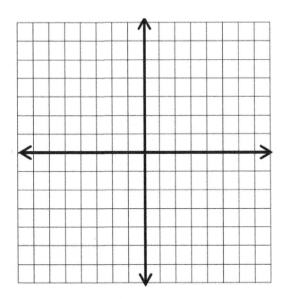

Rate of change

✎ **What is the average rate of change of the function?**

1) $f(x) = 3x^2 + 5$, from $x = 3$ to $x = 6$?

2) $f(x) = -2x^2 - 4$, from $x = 2$ to $x = 4$?

3) $f(x) = x^3 + 3$, from $x = 1$ to $x = 2$?

x and y intercepts

✎ **Find the x and y intercepts for the following equations.**

1) $5x + 3y = 15$

2) $y = x + 8$

3) $4x = y + 16$

4) $x + y = -2$

5) $4x - 3y = 7$

6) $7y - 5x + 10 = 0$

7) $\frac{3}{7}x + \frac{1}{4}y + \frac{2}{3} = 0$

8) $3x - 21 = 0$

9) $24 - 4y = 0$

10) $-2x - 6y + 42 = 12$

Slope–intercept Form

✎ **Write the slope–intercept form of the equation of each line.**

1) $-14x + y = 6$

2) $-2(7x + y) = 24$

3) $-8x - 16y = -48$

4) $5x + 14 = -3y$

5) $x - 3y = 12$

6) $18x - 12y = -6$

7) $28x - 14y = -56$

8) $7x - 4y + 25 = 0$

9) $-\frac{1}{3}y = -2x + 3$

10) $5 - y - 4x = 0$

11) $-y = -6x - 9$

12) $10x + 5y = -15$

13) $3(x + y + 2) = 0$

14) $y - 4 = x + 3$

15) $3(y + 3) = 2(x - 3)$

16) $\frac{3}{4}y + \frac{1}{4}x + \frac{5}{4} = 0$

Point–slope Form

✍ **Find the slope of the following lines. Name a point on each line.**

1) $y = 2(x + 3)$

6) $y - 8 = -3x$

2) $y + 4 = \dfrac{1}{3}(x - 1)$

7) $y - 12 = -3(x - 8)$

3) $y + 3 = -1.5x$

8) $y + 14 = 0$

4) $y - 3 = \dfrac{1}{2}(x - 2)$

9) $y + 18 = 2(x + 5)$

5) $y + 2 = 0.4(x + 3)$

10) $y - 17 = -8(x - 3)$

✍ **Write an equation in point–slope form for the line that passes**

through the given point with the slope provided.

11) $(2, -3), m = 4$

16) $(3, 0), m = -5$

12) $(-7, 4), m = \dfrac{1}{5}$

17) $(-4, 11), m = \dfrac{1}{3}$

13) $(0, -6), m = -2$

18) $(0, 11), m = 0$

14) $(-a, b), m = m$

19) $\left(-\dfrac{1}{3}, 3\right), m = \dfrac{1}{5}$

15) $(-9, 1), m = 3$

20) $(0, 0), m = -3$

Equation of Parallel or Perpendicular Lines

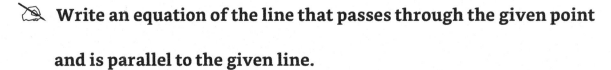 Write an equation of the line that passes through the given point

and is parallel to the given line.

1) $(-1, -2), x + 3y = -11$

2) $(-4, 1), y = x - 5$

3) $(-2, 0), 2y = 5x - 3$

4) $(0, 0), -3y + 4x - 14 = 0$

5) $(1, 10), y + 15 = 0$

6) $(0, 7), -5x - y = -4$

7) $(-2, -1), y = \frac{4}{5}x + 3$

8) $(-2, 5), -8x + 5y = -18$

9) $(3, -2), y = -\frac{2}{5}x - 3$

10) $(-5, -5), 6x + 15y = -30$

Write an equation of the line that passes through the given point

and is perpendicular to the given line.

11) $(-2, -6), 3x + 4y = -8$

12) $(-\frac{1}{3}, \frac{3}{5}), 4x - 8y = -32$

13) $(2, -5), y = -5$

14) $(7, -2), x = 7$

15) $(0, -3), y = \frac{1}{2}x + 6$

16) $(\frac{3}{5}, \frac{2}{5}), y = -6x - 24$

17) $(-10, 0), y = \frac{5}{3}x - 15$

18) $(3, -5), y = x + 12$

19) $(-3, -1), y = \frac{7}{3}x - 4$

20) $(0, 0), y - 8x + 6 = 0$

Graphing Absolute Value Equations

 Graph each equation.

1) $y = |x + 4|$

2) $y = |x + 1|$

3) $y = -|x| - 1$

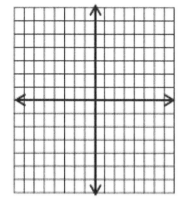 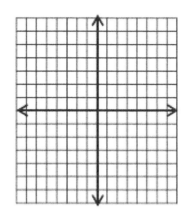 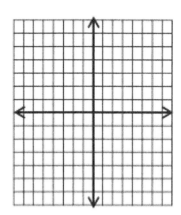

4) $y = |x - 2|$

5) $y = -|x - 2|$

6) $y = -2|2x + 2| + 4$

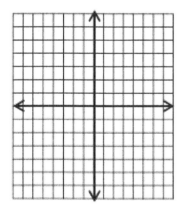 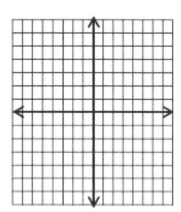 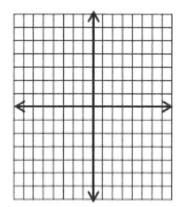

Answers of Worksheets

Finding Slope

1) 1

2) −3

3) 2

4) −4

5) 6

6) −5

7) 8

8) −9

9) −7

10) 3

11) $\frac{1}{3}$

12) $-\frac{4}{5}$

13) $\frac{1}{2}$

14) −1

15) $\frac{1}{3}$

16) $\frac{1}{8}$

17) $\frac{7}{5}$

18) 2

19) −3

20) 2

21) −1

22) 2

23) 2

24) −3

25) −1

26) $\frac{5}{2}$

27) 2

28) −11

Graphing Linear Equations

1) $y = x - 2$

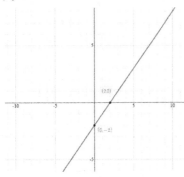

2) $y = -3x + 2$

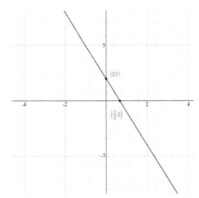

3) $x + y = 0$

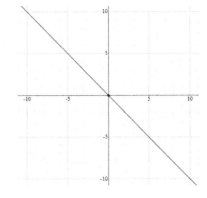

4) $x + y = -3$

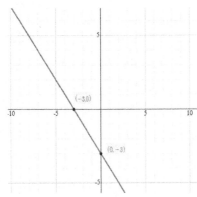

5) $2x + 3y = -4$

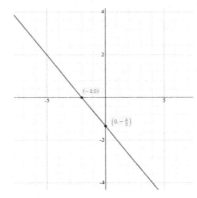

6) $y - 3x + 6 = 0$

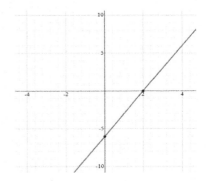

Graphing Linear Inequalities

1) $y > 4x - 5$

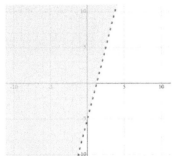

2) $y < 2x + 4$

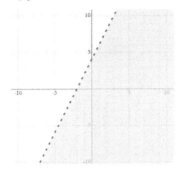

3) $y \leq -5x - 2$

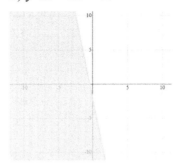

4) $4y \geq 12 + 4x$

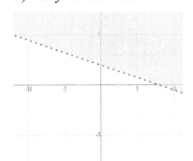

5) $-12y < 3x - 24$

6) $5y \geq -15x + 10$

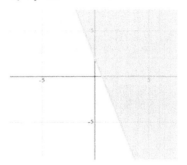

Writing Linear Equations

1) $y = 14x - 33$

2) $y = x + 9$

3) $y = -4x + 47$

4) $y = x - 4$

5) $y = 2x - 31$

6) $y = 9x - 43$

7) $y = -2x + 24$

8) $y = -3x + 1$

9) $y = -2x + 5$

10) $y = -2x + 6$

11) $y = 5x - 18$

12) $y = 14x - 122$

13) $y = 13x + 52$

14) $y = x + 10$

15) $y = -5x + 58$

16) $y = -5x + 5$

17) $y = 6x + 12$

18) $y = -11x - 4$

19) $y = -3x + 17$

20) $y = -5x - 11$

21) $y = -10x - 30$

22) $y = 8x + 7$

Find the value of b

1) -7

2) 11

3) 4

4) 3

Write an equation from a graph

1) $y = 2x + 4$

2) $y = 3x + 5$

3) $y = 5x$

4) $y = 2x + 5$

Graphing horizontal and vertical lines

1) $y = 3$ 2) $y = -1$ (it is on x axes)

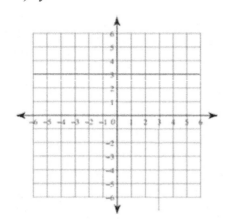   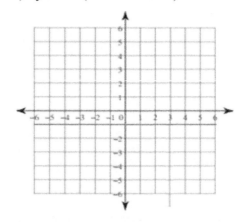

3) $x = 0$ 4) $x = 3$

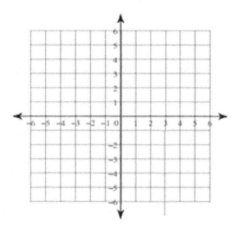   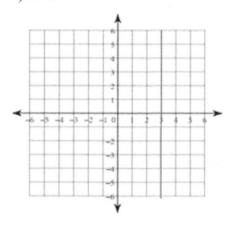

Rate of change

1) 27   2) -12 3) 7

x–intercept and y–intercept

1) $y - \text{intercept} = 5$ $x - \text{intercept} = 3$

2) $y - \text{intercept} = 8$ $x - \text{intercept} = -8$

3) $y - \text{intercept} = -16$ $x - \text{intercept} = 4$

4) $y - \text{intercept} = -2$ $x - \text{intercept} = -2$

5) $y - \text{intercept} = -\frac{7}{3}$ $x - \text{intercept} = \frac{7}{4}$

6) $y - \text{intercept} = -\frac{10}{7}$ $x - \text{intercept} = 2$

7) $y - \text{intercept} = -\frac{8}{3}$ $x - \text{intercept} = -\frac{2}{7}$

8) $y - \text{intercept} = \text{undefind}$ $x - \text{intercept} = 7$

9) y − intercept = 6   x − intercept = undefind

10) y − intercept = 5   x − intercept = 15

Slope–intercept form

1) $y = 14x + 6$

2) $y = -7x - 12$

3) $y = -\frac{1}{2}x + 3$

4) $y = -\frac{5}{3}x - \frac{14}{3}$

5) $y = \frac{x}{3} - 4$

6) $y = \frac{3}{2}x + \frac{1}{2}$

7) $y = 2x + 4$

8) $y = \frac{7}{4}x + \frac{25}{4}$

9) $y = 6x - 9$

10) $y = -4x + 5$

11) $y = 6x + 9$

12) $y = -2x - 3$

13) $y = -x - 2$

14) $y = x + 7$

15) $y = \frac{2}{3}x - 5$

16) $y = -\frac{1}{3}x - \frac{5}{3}$

Point–slope form

1) $m = 2, (-3, 0)$

2) $m = \frac{1}{3}, (1, -4)$

3) $m = -\frac{3}{2}, (0, -3)$

4) $m = \frac{1}{2}, (2, 3)$

5) $m = \frac{4}{10}, (-3, -2)$

6) $m = -3, (0, 8)$

7) $m = -3, (8, 12)$

8) $m = 0, (0, -14)$

9) $m = 2, (-5, -18)$

10) $m = -8, (-3, 17)$

11) $y + 3 = 4(x - 2)$

12) $y - 4 = \frac{1}{5}(x + 7)$

13) $y + 6 = -2x$

14) $y - b = m(x + a)$

15) $y - 1 = 3(x + 9)$

16) $y = -5(x - 3)$

17) $y - 11 = \frac{1}{3}(x + 4)$

18) $y - 11 = 0$

19) $y - 3 = \frac{1}{5}\left(x + \frac{1}{3}\right)$

20) $y = -3x$

Equation of Parallel or Perpendicular Lines.

1) $y = -\frac{1}{3}x - 2\frac{1}{3}$

2) $y = x + 5$

3) $y = \frac{5}{2}x + 5$

4) $y = \frac{4}{3}x$

5) $y = 10$

6) $y = -5x + 7$

7) $y = \frac{4}{5}x + \frac{3}{5}$

8) $y = \frac{8}{5}x + \frac{41}{5}$

9) $y = -\frac{2}{5}x - \frac{4}{5}$

10) $y = -\frac{2}{5}x - 7$

11) $y = \frac{4}{3}x - \frac{10}{3}$

12) $y = -2x - \frac{1}{15}$

13) $x = 2$

14) $y = -2$

15) $y = -2x - 3$

16) $y = \frac{1}{6}x + \frac{3}{10}$

17) $y = -\frac{3}{5}x - 6$

18) $y = -x - 2$

19) $y = -\frac{3}{7}x - \frac{16}{7}$ 20) $y = -\frac{1}{8}x$

Graphing Absolute Value Equations

1) $y = |x + 4|$ 2) $y = |x - 1|$ 3) $y = -|x| - 1$

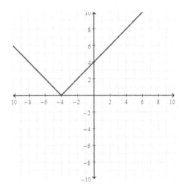 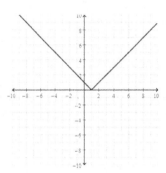 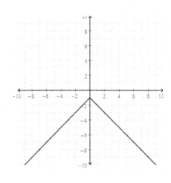

4) $y = |x - 2|$ 5) $y = -|x - 2|$ 6) $y = -2|2x + 2| + 4$

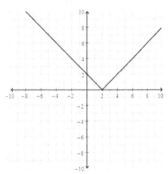 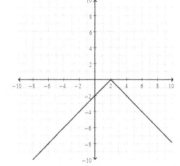 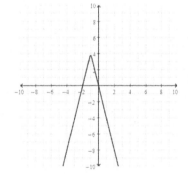

Chapter 8 :

Equations and Inequalities

Topics that you'll practice in this chapter:

- ✓ One–Step Equations
- ✓ Multi–Step Equations
- ✓ Graphing Single–Variable Inequalities
- ✓ One–Step Inequalities
- ✓ Multi-Step Inequalities
- ✓ Systems of Equations
- ✓ Systems of Equations Word Problems
- ✓ Finding Midpoint
- ✓ Finding Distance of Two Points

"Life is a math equation. In order to gain the most, you have to know how to convert negatives into positives." – Anonymous

One–Step Equations

✏️ Find the answer for each equation.

1) $3x = 90, x =$ ___

2) $5x = 35, x =$ ___

3) $6x = 24, x =$ ___

4) $24x = 144, x =$ ___

5) $x + 15 = 20, x =$ ___

6) $x - 7 = 4, x =$ ___

7) $x - 9 = 2, x =$ ___

8) $x + 15 = 23, x =$ ___

9) $x - 4 = 13, x =$ ___

10) $12 = 16 + x, x =$ ___

11) $x - 10 = 2, x =$ ___

12) $5 - x = -11, x =$ ___

13) $28 = -6 + x, x =$ ___

14) $x - 20 = -35, x =$ ___

15) $x + 14 = -4, x =$ ___

16) $14 = 28 - x, x =$ ___

17) $7 + x = -7, x =$ ___

18) $x - 16 = 4, x =$ ___

19) $30 = x - 15, x =$ ___

20) $x - 5 = -18, x =$ ___

21) $x - 10 = 24, x =$ ___

22) $x - 20 = -25, x =$ ___

23) $x - 17 = 30, x =$ ___

24) $-70 = x - 28, x =$ ___

25) $x - 9 = 13, x =$ ___

26) $36 = 4x, x =$ ___

27) $x - 35 = 25, x =$ ___

28) $x - 25 = 10, x =$ ___

29) $70 - x = 16, x =$ ___

30) $x - 10 = 14, x =$ ___

31) $17 - x = -13, x =$ __

32) $x - 9 = -30, x =$ ___

Multi–Step Equations

✍ **Find the answer for each equation.**

1) $3x + 3 = 9$

2) $-x + 5 = 12$

3) $4x - 8 = 8$

4) $-(3 - x) = 5$

5) $4x - 8 = 16$

6) $12x - 15 = 9$

7) $2x - 18 = 2$

8) $4x + 8 = 16$

9) $24x + 27 = 75$

10) $-14(3 + x) = 14$

11) $-3(2 + x) = 6$

12) $12 = -(x - 7)$

13) $3(3 - x) = 30$

14) $-15 = -(3x + 6)$

15) $40(3 + x) = 40$

16) $5(x - 10) = 25$

17) $-18 = x + 8x$

18) $3x + 25 = -2x - 10$

19) $7(6 + 3x) = -63$

20) $18 - 3x = -4 - 5x$

21) $4 - 6x = 36 + 2x$

22) $15 + 15x = -5 + 5x$

23) $42 = (-6x) - 7 + 7$

24) $21 = 3x - 21 + 4x$

25) $-18 = -6x - 9 + 3x$

26) $5x - 15 = -29 + 6x$

27) $7x - 18 = 4x + 3$

28) $-7 - 4x = 5(4 - x)$

29) $x - 5 = -5(-3 - x)$

30) $13x - 68 = 15x - 102$

31) $-5x - 3 = -3(9 + 3x)$

32) $-2x - 15 = 6x + 17$

Graphing Single–Variable Inequalities

✎ **Draw a graph for each inequality.**

1) $x > -1$

2) $x \leq 2$

3) $x \geq 0$

4) $x < -3$

5) $x < \dfrac{1}{2}$

6) $x \leq -2$

7) $x \leq 3$

8) $x \geq -\dfrac{7}{2}$

One–Step Inequalities

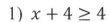 **Find the answer for each inequality and graph it.**

1) $x + 4 \geq 4$

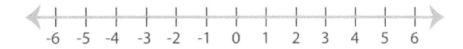

2) $x - 5 \leq 2$

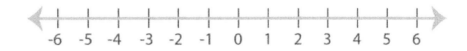

3) $5x > 35$

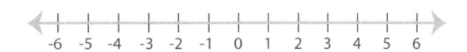

4) $9 + x \leq 11$

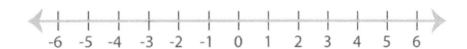

5) $x - 5 < -9$

6) $9x \geq 72$

7) $9x \leq 27$

8) $x + 19 > 16$

Multi-Step Inequalities

✏️ Calculate each inequality.

1) $x - 3 \leq 7$

2) $8 - x \leq 8$

3) $3x - 9 \leq 9$

4) $4x - 4 \geq 8$

5) $x - 7 \geq 1$

6) $5x - 15 \leq 5$

7) $6x - 8 \leq 4$

8) $-11 + 6x \leq 12$

9) $4(x - 4) \leq 16$

10) $3x - 10 \leq 11$

11) $5x - 25 < 25$

12) $9x - 5 < 22$

13) $20 - 7x \geq -15$

14) $33 + 6x < 45$

15) $8 + 8x \geq 96$

16) $7 + 3x < 13$

17) $4x - 3 < 9$

18) $5(2 - 2x) \geq -30$

19) $-(7 + 6x) < 29$

20) $12 - 8x \geq -20$

21) $-4(x - 6) > 24$

22) $\dfrac{3x + 9}{6} \leq 10$

23) $\dfrac{4x - 10}{3} \leq 2$

24) $\dfrac{2x - 8}{3} > 2$

25) $8 + \dfrac{x}{6} < 9$

26) $\dfrac{9x}{7} - 4 < 5$

27) $\dfrac{15x + 45}{15} > 1$

28) $16 + \dfrac{x}{4} < 6$

Solving Systems of Equations by Substitution

✎ Solve each system of equation by substitution.

1) $-x + 3y = -6$

$$x - 2y = 7$$

2) $4x + 2y = -4$

$$-x - 2y = 5$$

3) $2x + 3y = -4$

$$3x - y = 8$$

4) $y = -2x + 3$

$$2x - y = -5$$

5) $4x = 8$

$$5y = 3x + 4$$

6) $4x + 3y = 5$

$$2x + y = -8$$

7) $3x + 2y = 1$

$$x + y = -6$$

8) $3y = x + 2$

$$2x - y = -4$$

Solving Systems of Equations by Elimination

✏️ Solve each system of equation by elimination.

1) $-4x + y = -4$

$$-y = -3x + 3$$

2) $-x - 3y = -1$

$$x - 2y = 6$$

3) $2x - y = 5$

$$-x + 3y = -5$$

4) $x - y = -12$

$$-2x - 3y = 4$$

5) $7x + 2y = -15$

$$3x - y = -12$$

6) $2x - 3y = -8$

$$x + 2y = 10$$

7) $-3x + 15y = -3$

$$2x - 3y = 9$$

8) $3x - 4y = -6$

$$6x + 5y = -12$$

Systems of Equations Word Problems

✎ **Find the answer for each word problem.**

1) Tickets to a movie cost $4 for adults and $3 for students. A group of friends purchased 8 tickets for $31.00. How many adults ticket did they buy? ____

2) At a store, Eva bought two shirts and five hats for $77.00. Nicole bought three same shirts and four same hats for $84.00. What is the price of each shirt? _____

3) A farmhouse shelters 18 animals, some are pigs, and some are ducks. Altogether there are 66 legs. How many pigs are there? _____

4) A class of 214 students went on a field trip. They took 36 vehicles, some cars and some buses. If each car holds 5 students and each bus hold 22 students, how many buses did they take? _____

5) A theater is selling tickets for a performance. Mr. Smith purchased 5 senior tickets and 3 child tickets for $105 for his friends and family. Mr. Jackson purchased 3 senior tickets and 5 child tickets for $79. What is the price of a senior ticket? $_____

6) The difference of two numbers is 10. Their sum is 20. What is the bigger number? $_____

7) The sum of the digits of a certain two–digit number is 7. Reversing its digits increase the number by 9. What is the number? _____

8) The difference of two numbers is 11. Their sum is 25. What are the numbers? _____

9) The length of a rectangle is 5 meters greater than 2 times the width. The perimeter of rectangle is 28 meters. What is the length of the rectangle? _____

10) Jim has 25 nickels and dimes totaling $1.80. How many nickels does he have? _____

Finding Midpoint

✎ **Find the midpoint of the line segment with the given endpoints.**

1) $(-4, -3), (2, 3)$

2) $(9, 0), (-1, 8)$

3) $(9, -6), (3, 14)$

4) $(-10, -6), (0, 8)$

5) $(2, -5), (14, -15)$

6) $(-10, -3), (4, -13)$

7) $(8, 7), (-8, 13)$

8) $(-3, 6), (-9, 2)$

9) $(-4, 5), (16, -9)$

10) $(7, 14), (9, -2)$

11) $(-8, 6), (6, 6)$

12) $(10, 5), (-2, -3)$

13) $(-5, 12), (-3, 3)$

14) $(12, 7), (8, -2)$

15) $(10, 2), (-6, 14)$

16) $(-1, -2), (-7, 10)$

17) $(7, -7), (13, -13)$

18) $(-3, -8), (11, -4)$

19) $(5, -11), (-8, 9)$

20) $(14, -4), (16, 14)$

21) $(0, -5), (8, -1)$

22) $(3, 0), (-21, 18)$

23) $(17, -3), (-7, -5)$

24) $(26, -12), (6, 24)$

✎ **Find the answer for each problem.**

25) One endpoint of a line segment is $(-3, 7)$ and the midpoint of the line segment is $(-6, 9)$. What is the other endpoint? _____

26) One endpoint of a line segment is $(-3, 7)$ and the midpoint of the line segment is $(1, 5)$. What is the other endpoint? _____

27) One endpoint of a line segment is $(-10, -16)$ and the midpoint of the line segment is $(2, 9)$. What is the other endpoint? _____

Finding Distance of Two Points

✎ **Find the distance between each pair of points.**

1) $(6, 3), (-3, -9)$

2) $(5, 2), (-10, -6)$

3) $(8, 5), (8, 3)$

4) $(-8, -2), (2, 22)$

5) $(6, -7), (-3, -7)$

6) $(12, 0), (-9, -20)$

7) $(3, 20), (3, -5)$

8) $(10, 17), (5, 5)$

9) $(7, -2), (-4, -2)$

10) $(13, 4), (5, -2)$

11) $(11, 13), (5, 5)$

12) $(1, 4), (-23, -3)$

13) $(9, 8), (5, -4)$

14) $(-11, -4), (5, 8)$

15) $(-2, -6), (-2, -12)$

16) $(-1, -4), (23, 3)$

17) $(19, 3), (7, -6)$

18) $(-5, -2), (3, 4)$

19) $(2, 6), (2, -12)$

20) $(-4, -2), (8, -2)$

✎ **Find the answer for each problem.**

21) Triangle ABC is a right triangle on the coordinate system and its vertices are $(-2, 5)$, $(-2, 1)$, and $(1, 1)$. What is the area of triangle ABC? _____

22) Three vertices of a triangle on a coordinate system are $(3, -6)$, $(-5, -12)$, and $(3, -18)$. What is the perimeter of the triangle? _____

23) Four vertices of a rectangle on a coordinate system are $(-2, 2)$, $(-2, 6)$, $(4, 2)$, and $(4, 6)$. What is its perimeter? _____

Answers of Worksheets

One–Step Equations

1) 30	9) 17	17) −14	25) 22
2) 7	10) −4	18) 20	26) 9
3) 4	11) 12	19) 45	27) 60
4) 6	12) 16	20) −13	28) 35
5) 5	13) 34	21) 34	29) 54
6) 11	14) −15	22) −5	30) 24
7) 11	15) −18	23) 47	31) 30
8) 8	16) 14	24) −42	32) −21

Multi–Step Equations

1) 2	9) 2	17) −2	25) 3
2) −7	10) −4	18) −7	26) 14
3) 4	11) −4	19) −5	27) 7
4) 8	12) −5	20) −11	28) 27
5) 6	13) −7	21) −4	29) −5
6) 2	14) 3	22) −2	30) 17
7) 10	15) −2	23) −7	31) −6
8) 2	16) 15	24) 6	32) −4

Graphing Single–Variable Inequalities

1)

2)

3)

4)

5)

6)

7)

8)

One–Step Inequalities

1)

2)

3)

4)

5)

6)

7)

8)

Multi-Step Inequalities

1) $x \leq 10$

2) $x \geq 0$

3) $x \leq 6$

4) $x \geq 3$

5) $x \geq 8$

6) $x \leq 4$

7) $x \leq 2$

8) $x \leq \frac{23}{6}$

9) $x \leq 8$

10) $x \leq 7$

11) $x < 10$

12) $x < 3$

13) $x \leq 5$

14) $x < 2$

15) $x \geq 11$

16) $x < 2$

17) $x < 3$

18) $x \leq 4$

19) $x > -6$

20) $x \leq 4$

21) $x < 0$

22) $x \leq 17$

23) $x \leq 4$

24) $x > 7$ 26) $x < 7$ 28) $x < -40$

25) $x < 6$ 27) $x > -2$

Solving Systems of Equations by Substitution

1) $(9, 1)$ 3) $(\frac{20}{11}, -\frac{28}{11})$ 5) $(2, 2)$ 7) $(13, -19)$

2) $(\frac{1}{3}, -\frac{8}{3})$ 4) $(-\frac{1}{2}, 4)$ 6) $(-\frac{29}{2}, 21)$ 8) $(-2, 0)$

Solving Systems of Equations by Elimination

1) $(1, 0)$ 3) $(2, -1)$ 5) $(-3, 3)$ 7) $(6, 1)$

2) $(4, -1)$ 4) $(-8, 4)$ 6) $(2, 4)$ 8) $(-2, 0)$

Systems of Equations Word Problems

1) 7   4) 2   7) 34   10) 14

2) $16   5) $18   8) 18, 7

3) 15   6) 15   9) 11 meters

Finding Midpoint

1) $(-1, 0)$ 10) $(8, 6)$ 19) $(-1.5, -1)$

2) $(4, 4)$ 11) $(-1, 6)$ 20) $(15, 5)$

3) $(6, 4)$ 12) $(4, 1)$ 21) $(4, -3)$

4) $(-5, 1)$ 13) $(-4, 7.5)$ 22) $(-9, 9)$

5) $(8, -10)$ 14) $(10, 2.5)$ 23) $(5, -4)$

6) $(-3, -8)$ 15) $(2, 8)$ 24) $(16, 6)$

7) $(0, 10)$ 16) $(-4, 4)$ 25) $(-9, 11)$

8) $(-6, 4)$ 17) $(10, -10)$ 26) $(5, 3)$

9) $(6, -2)$ 18) $(4, -6)$ 27) $(14, 34)$

Finding Distance of Two Points

1) 15   6) 29   11) 10   16) 25

2) 17   7) 25   12) 25   17) 15

3) 2   8) 13   13) $4\sqrt{10}$ 18) 10

4) 26   9) 11   14) 20   19) 18

5) 9   10) 10   15) 6   20) 12

21) 6 *square units*   22) 32 *units*   23) 20 *units*

Chapter 9 :

Monomials and Polynomials

Topics that you'll practice in this chapter:

- ✓ GCF of Monomials
- ✓ Factoring Quadratics
- ✓ Factoring by Grouping
- ✓ GCF and Powers of Monomials
- ✓ Writing Polynomials in Standard Form
- ✓ Simplifying Polynomials
- ✓ Adding and Subtracting Polynomials
- ✓ Multiplying Monomials
- ✓ Multiplying and Dividing Monomials
- ✓ Multiplying a Polynomial and a Monomial
- ✓ Multiplying Binomials
- ✓ Factoring Trinomials
- ✓ Operations with Polynomials

Mathematics is, as it were, a sensuous logic, and relates to philosophy as do the arts, music, and plastic art to poetry. — K. Shegel

GCF of Monomials

✎ **Find the GCF of each set of monomials.**

1) $26xy, 14x$

2) $40a, 16a^2$

3) $15x^3, 45x^3$

4) $48x^4, 36x^6$

5) $10a^2, 40a^2b$

6) $70a^2, 20a^2b$

7) $32x^2, 24x^2$

8) $55x, 77y^4x$

9) $18, 24x^2, 36$

10) $15v^2, 60v, 45v$

11) p^3q^3, pqn

12) $12m^3n, 18m^3n^3$

13) $15x^3y, 5xy^3z$

14) $44m^2n^3, 66m^4n^5$

15) $28x^4y, 21x^3$

16) $18ab^6, 8a^3b^3c$

17) $25t^2u^3, 35t^4u^2$

18) $16t, 64t^2$

19) $14r^5q, 28pr^3t^2$

20) $20ab^4, 60a^3b$

21) $12d, 42ab^3$

22) $16a^2b^2, 24bc$

23) $10db, 35db$

24) $21m^2n^3, 42m^3n^2$

25) $8xyz, 4x^2$

26) $6x^2yz^{10}, 2x^2yz^4$

27) $120xz, 120y^3, 30y^3$

28) $32b, 40b, 32cb^2$

29) $20x^4, 15x^4, 25x$

30) $110b, 80bc, 70b$

Factoring Quadratics

✎ **Factor each completely.**

1) $x^2 - 13x + 40 =$

2) $m^2 - 11m + 18 =$

3) $p^2 + 2p - 48 =$

4) $3b^2 + 29b + 40 =$

5) $a^2 - 4a + 3 =$

6) $a^2 - 7a + 10 =$

7) $5n^2 - 28n + 32 =$

8) $t^2 - 11t + 28 =$

9) $4x^3 - 27x^2 + 18x =$

10) $x^2 - 10x + 21 =$

11) $7r^2 - 37r + 36 =$

12) $4n^2b - 37nb + 40b =$

13) $3x^2 - 44x + 96 =$

14) $b^3 - 12b^2 + 27b =$

15) $5m^2 - 48m + 27 =$

16) $2x^3 - 23x^2 + 56x =$

17) $x^2 - 13x + 42 =$

18) $p^2 - 13p + 12 =$

19) $x^2 - 14x + 24 =$

20) $8x^2 - 59x + 21 =$

21) $12n^2 - 7n - 10 =$

22) $-3x^2 - 28x - 49 =$

23) $-8x^2 - 2x + 3 =$

24) $6x^2 + 13x - 63 =$

25) $12x^2 - 68x + 40 =$

26) $7x^2 - 48x + 36 =$

27) $8n^2 + 76n + 96 =$

28) $5x^2 - 18x + 9 =$

29) $5x^2 - 35xy =$

30) $-10x^3 - 124x^2y - 48y^2x =$

31) $16a^2 + 8ab - 15b^2 =$

32) $25x^2 - 10xy - 8y^2 =$

33) $64x^2y - 152xy^2 + 90y^3 =$

34) $3x^2 - 12xy - 63y^2 =$

35) $56mp^2 - 49mp =$

36) $27b^2 + 150b + 75 =$

37) $12x^2 + 90xy + 162y^2 =$

38) $16x^2 + 14xy =$

Factoring by Grouping

✎ **Factor each completely.**

1) $18xy - 24x + 3ky - 4k =$

2) $12xy - 10x + 6ny - 5n =$

3) $15n^3 + 10n^2 + 6n + 4 =$

4) $9u^2v + 36u^4 - 6umv - 24u^3m =$

5) $24n^4 + 8n^3 + 36n^2 + 12n =$

6) $16uv - 8u^2 + 24bv - 12bu =$

7) $2x^3 + 6x^2 + 9x + 27 =$

8) $4x^3 + 16x^2 + 8x + 32 =$

9) $3m^3 - 3m^2 + 6m - 6 =$

10) $3x^3 - 9x^2 - 18x + 54 =$

11) $6p^3 + 8p^2 - 15p - 20 =$

12) $18mc + 8md - 9n^2c - 4n^2d =$

13) $16x^4 + 32x^2 - 40x^2 - 80x =$

14) $8xw + 10kx + 12yw + 15ky =$

15) $25xy - 10x + 15ry - 6r =$

16) $3xy - 6x - 7y + 14 =$

17) $5x^3 - 40x^2 + 2x - 16 =$

18) $18x^3 - 126x^2 + 3x - 21 =$

19) $6x^3 + 21x^2 + 10x + 35 =$

20) $12x^3 + 36x^2 - 30x - 90 =$

GCF and Powers of Monomials

✎ **Find the GCF of each pairs of expressions.**

1) $45x^4, 18x^4$

2) $66y, 88y^2x$

3) $18x^2, 24, 36$

4) $20a^3, 55a^2, 15a$

5) xp^3q^3, pq

6) $10m^2n, 45m^2n^2$

7) $15yz, 5xy^2$

8) $24m^8n^3, 16m^2n^2$

9) $18x^4, 27x^2y$

10) $12cb^5, 6a^2b^2c$

11) $15t^2u^6, 20t^4u^7$

12) $17t, 51t^6$

13) $19r^2tq, 38r^4t^9$

14) $12a^2b^9, 36a^8b^5$

15) $14f, 25ab^3$

16) $15a^3b^3c^2, 22abc$

17) $10ab, 5ab$

18) $32m^6n^2, 16m^3n^4$

19) $6xy, 3x^2$

20) $x^2yz^3, 3x^2yz^3$

✎ **Simplify.**

21) $(2x^5)^3$

22) $(2y^33y^2y)^3$

23) $(4x^33x^3)^2$

24) $(5x^2y^4)^4$

25) $(2y^22y^3)^5$

26) $(3x^2y)^7$

27) $(5x^3x^32n)^3$

28) $(4xy^4)^6$

29) $(8x^4y^2)^3$

30) $(14y^5y^2)^2$

31) $(5x^3x^4)^4$

32) $(2x^86x^2k^3)^2$

33) $(y^63y^2)^3$

34) $(2x2x^4)^7$

35) $(8y^6)^2$

36) $(2y^2y^5y^2)^4$

37) $(6y^3y)^4$

38) $(5xy^5)^4$

Writing Polynomials in Standard Form

✎ **Write each polynomial in standard form.**

1) $11x - 7x =$

2) $-5 + 19x - 19x =$

3) $6x^5 - 12x^3 =$

4) $12 + 17x^4 - 12 =$

5) $5x^2 + 4x - 9x^3 =$

6) $-3x^2 + 12x^5 =$

7) $5x + 8x^3 - 2x^8 =$

8) $-7x^3 + 4x - 9x^6 =$

9) $3x^2 + 22 - 6x =$

10) $3 - 4x + 9x^4 =$

11) $13x^2 + 28x - 8x^3 =$

12) $16 + 4x^2 - 2x^3 =$

13) $19x^2 - 9x + 9x^4 =$

14) $3x^4 - 7x^2 - 2x^3 =$

15) $-51 + 3x^2 - 8x^4 =$

16) $7x^2 - 8x^6 + 4x^4 - 15 =$

17) $6x^4 - 4x^5 + 16 - 3x^3 =$

18) $-2x^6 + 4x - 7x^2 - 5x =$

19) $11x^7 + 8x^5 - 5x^7 - 3x^2 =$

20) $2x^2 - 12x^5 + 8x^2 + 3x^6 =$

21) $4x^5 - 11x^7 - 6x^3 + 16x^5 =$

22) $6x^3 + 3x^5 + 34x^4 - 8x^5 =$

23) $3x(4x + 5 - 2x^2) =$

24) $12x(x^6 + 4x^3) =$

25) $5x(3x^2 + 6x + 4) =$

26) $7x(4 - 2x + 6x^5) =$

27) $3x(4x^4 - 4x^3 + 2) =$

28) $4x(2x^5 + 6x^2 - 3) =$

29) $5x(3x^4 + 4x^3 + 2x) =$

30) $2x(3x - 2x^3 + 4x^6) =$

Simplifying Polynomials

✎ **Simplify each expression.**

1) $3(4x - 20) =$

2) $5x(3x - 4) =$

3) $6x(5x - 7) =$

4) $3x(7x + 5) =$

5) $5x(4x - 3) =$

6) $6x(8x + 2) =$

7) $(3x - 2)(x - 4) =$

8) $(x - 5)(2x + 6) =$

9) $(x - 3)(x - 7) =$

10) $(3x + 4)(3x - 4) =$

11) $(5x - 4)(5x - 2) =$

12) $6x^2 + 6x^2 - 8x^4 =$

13) $3x - 2x^2 + 5x^3 + 7 =$

14) $7x + 4x^2 - 10x^3 =$

15) $12x^2 + 5x^5 - 6x^3 =$

16) $-5x^2 + 4x^6 + 6x^8 =$

17) $-12x^3 + 10x^5 - 4x^6 + 4x =$

18) $11 - 7x^2 + 4x^2 - 16x^3 + 11 =$

19) $2x^2 - 9x + 4x^3 + 15x - 10x =$

20) $13 - 7x^5 + 6x^5 - 4x^2 + 5 =$

21) $-5x^8 + x^6 - 14x^3 + 5x^8 =$

22) $(7x^4 - 4) + (7x^4 - 2x^4) =$

23) $3(3x^4 - 4x^3 - 6x^4) =$

24) $-5(x^9 + 8) - 5(10 - x^9) =$

25) $8x^3 - 9x^4 - 2x + 19 - 8x^3 =$

26) $11 - 8x^3 + 6x^3 - 7x^5 + 6 =$

27) $(5x^3 - 4x) - (6x - 2 - 6x^3) =$

28) $4x^2 - 5x^4 - x(3x^3 + 2x) =$

29) $6x + 6x^5 - 10 - 4(x^5 - 3) =$

30) $4 - 3x^4 + (6x^5 - 2x^4 + 5x^5) =$

31) $-(x^5 + 4) - 8(3 + x^5) =$

32) $(4x^3 - 3x) - (3x - 5x^3) =$

Adding and Subtracting Polynomials

✎ Add or subtract expressions.

1) $(-2x^2 - 3) + (3x^2 + 4) =$

2) $(4x^3 + 6) - (7 - 2x^3) =$

3) $(4x^5 + 5x^2) - (2x^5 + 15) =$

4) $(6x^3 - 2x^2) + (5x^2 - 4x) =$

5) $(10x^4 + 28x) - (34x^4 + 6) =$

6) $(7x^2 - 3) + (7x^2 + 3) =$

7) $(9x^2 + 4) - (10 - 5x^2) =$

8) $(6x^2 + x^5) - (x^5 + 4) =$

9) $(4x^3 - x) + (3x - 7x^3) =$

10) $(11x + 10) - (8x + 10) =$

11) $(15x^3 - 3x) - (3x - 4x^3) =$

12) $(4x - x^5) - (6x^5 + 8x) =$

13) $(2x^2 - 7x^7) - (4x^7 - 6x) =$

14) $(3x^2 - 5) + (8x^2 + 4x^5) =$

15) $(9x^4 + 5x^5) - (x^5 - 9x^4) =$

16) $(-4x^3 - 2x) + (9x - 5x^3) =$

17) $(4x - 3x^2) - (148x^2 + x) =$

18) $(5x - 8x^4) - (3x^4 - 4x^2) =$

19) $(8x^4 - 4) + (2x^4 - 3x^2) =$

20) $(5x^6 + 7x^3) - (x^3 - 5x^6) =$

21) $(-2x^2 + 20x^5 + 5x^4) + (12x^4 + 8x^5 + 24x^2) =$

22) $(7x^4 - 9x^7 - 6x) - (-3x^4 - 9x^7 + 6x) =$

23) $(14x + 12x^4 - 18x^6) + (20x^4 + 18x^6 - 10x) =$

24) $(5x^8 - 6x^6 - 4x) - (5x^3 + 9x^6 - 7x) =$

25) $(11x^2 - 6x^4 - 3x) - (-4x^2 - 12x^4 + 9x) =$

26) $(-5x^9 + 14x^3 + 3x^7) + (10x^7 + 26x^3 + 3x^9) =$

Multiplying Monomials

✎ **Simplify each expression.**

1) $6u^8 \times (-u^2) =$

2) $(-5p^8) \times (-2p^3) =$

3) $4xy^3z^5 \times 3z^4 =$

4) $3u^5t \times 8ut^4 =$

5) $(-5a^2) \times (-7a^3b^6) =$

6) $-3a^4b^3 \times 6a^2b =$

7) $13xy^5 \times x^4y^4 =$

8) $6p^4q^3 \times (-8pq^6) =$

9) $8s^4t^3 \times 4st^3 =$

10) $(-6x^4y^3) \times 6x^2y =$

11) $3xy^7z \times 12z^3 =$

12) $24xy \times x^2y =$

13) $13pq^4 \times (-3p^2q) =$

14) $13s^3t^4 \times st^4 =$

15) $11p^5 \times (-6p^3) =$

16) $(-8p^3q^5r) \times 3pq^4r^6 =$

17) $(-4a^4) \times (-7a^3b) =$

18) $6u^6v^2 \times (-5u^3v^4) =$

19) $9u^5 \times (-3u) =$

20) $-6xy^5 \times 4x^2y =$

21) $13y^5z^3 \times (-y^3z) =$

22) $8a^4bc^3 \times 2abc^3 =$

23) $(-7p^5q^6) \times (-5p^4q^2) =$

24) $4u^5v^3 \times (-4u^7v^3) =$

25) $17y^4z^5 \times (-y^6z) =$

26) $(-5pq^3r^2) \times 8p^2q^4r =$

27) $3ab^5c^6 \times 5a^4bc^2 =$

28) $6x^3yz^2 \times 3x^2y^7z^3 =$

Multiplying and Dividing Monomials

✏️ **Simplify each expression.**

1) $(5x^5)(2x^2) =$

2) $(4x^4)(6x^2) =$

3) $(3x^4)(7x^4) =$

4) $(5x^6)(4x^2) =$

5) $(12x^4)(3x^6) =$

6) $(4yx^8)(8y^4x^3) =$

7) $(14x^4y)(x^3y^5) =$

8) $(-5x^3y^4)(2x^3y^5) =$

9) $(-6x^4y^2)(-3x^3y^5) =$

10) $(5x^3y)(-5x^2y^3) =$

11) $(6x^4y^3)(4x^3y^4) =$

12) $(4x^3y^2)(5x^2y^4) =$

13) $(12x^3y^6)(4x^4y^{10}) =$

14) $(15x^3y^5)(3x^4y^6) =$

15) $(7x^2y^7)(8x^6y^7) =$

16) $(-3x^3y^8)(7x^9y^4) =$

17) $\dfrac{5x^6y^6}{xy^4} =$

18) $\dfrac{19x^7y^5}{19x^6y} =$

19) $\dfrac{56x^4y^4}{8xy} =$

20) $\dfrac{81x^5y^6}{9x^4y^5} =$

21) $\dfrac{36x^7y^6}{9x^2y^3} =$

22) $\dfrac{48x^9y^7}{4x^4y^6} =$

23) $\dfrac{88x^{18}y^{12}}{11x^8y^9} =$

24) $\dfrac{30x^7y^6}{6x^8y^3} =$

25) $\dfrac{150x^7y^6}{30x^4y^6} =$

26) $\dfrac{-42x^{18}y^{14}}{6x^4y^9} =$

27) $\dfrac{-36x^7y^8}{9x^5y^8} =$

Multiplying a Polynomial and a Monomial

✎ **Find each product.**

1) $x(2x + 4) =$

2) $6(4 - 2x) =$

3) $5x(4x + 2) =$

4) $x(-4x + 5) =$

5) $8x(2x - 2) =$

6) $6(2x - 4y) =$

7) $7x(5x - 5) =$

8) $3x(12x + 2y) =$

9) $4x(x + 6y) =$

10) $11x(3x + 4y) =$

11) $7x(3x + 2) =$

12) $10x(4x - 10y) =$

13) $9x(3x - 2y) =$

14) $7x(x - 4y + 6) =$

15) $8x(2x^2 + 5y^2) =$

16) $12x(2x + 3y) =$

17) $4(2x^4 - 4y^4) =$

18) $4x(-3x^2y + 4y) =$

19) $-4(5x^3 - 2xy + 4) =$

20) $4(x^2 - 5xy - 6) =$

21) $8x(2x^3 - 5xy + 2x) =$

22) $-6x(-2x^3 - 6x + 2xy) =$

23) $3(2x^2 + xy - 9y^2) =$

24) $4x(5x^3 - 3x + 7) =$

25) $6(3x^{22} - 2x - 5) =$

26) $x^2(-2x^3 + 4x + 3) =$

27) $x^2(4x^3 + 10 - 2x) =$

28) $4x^4(3x^3 - 2x + 5) =$

29) $2x^2(4x^4 - 5xy + 7y^3) =$

30) $5x^2(5x^4 - 3x + 9) =$

31) $7x^2(6x^2 + 3x - 6) =$

32) $4x(x^3 - 4xy + 2y^2) =$

Multiplying Binomials

✎ **Find each product.**

1) $(x + 3)(x + 6) =$

2) $(x - 4)(x + 3) =$

3) $(x - 3)(x - 8) =$

4) $(x + 8)(x + 9) =$

5) $(x - 2)(x - 12) =$

6) $(x + 5)(x + 5) =$

7) $(x - 6)(x + 7) =$

8) $(x - 8)(x - 3) =$

9) $(x + 7)(x + 12) =$

10) $(x - 4)(x + 8) =$

11) $(x + 8)(x + 8) =$

12) $(x + 2)(x + 7) =$

13) $(x - 6)(x + 6) =$

14) $(x - 5)(x + 5) =$

15) $(x + 11)(x + 11) =$

16) $(x + 6)(x + 9) =$

17) $(x - 2)(x + 2) =$

18) $(x - 4)(x + 7) =$

19) $(3x + 5)(x + 6) =$

20) $(5x - 6)(4x + 8) =$

21) $(x - 7)(3x + 7) =$

22) $(x - 9)(x - 4) =$

23) $(x - 12)(x + 2) =$

24) $(2x - 4)(5x + 4) =$

25) $(3x - 8)(x + 8) =$

26) $(7x - 2)(6x + 3) =$

27) $(4x + 5)(3x + 5) =$

28) $(7x - 4)(9x + 4) =$

29) $(x + 2)(2x - 8) =$

30) $(5x - 4)(5x + 4) =$

31) $(3x + 2)(3x - 7) =$

32) $(x^2 + 8)(x^2 - 8) =$

Factoring Trinomials

✎ **Factor each trinomial.**

1) $x^2 + 8x + 12 =$

2) $x^2 - 6x + 5 =$

3) $x^2 + 15x + 36 =$

4) $x^2 - 12x + 35 =$

5) $x^2 - 11x + 18 =$

6) $x^2 - 9x + 18 =$

7) $x^2 + 18x + 72 =$

8) $x^2 - x - 72 =$

9) $x^2 + 4x - 21 =$

10) $x^2 - 13x + 22 =$

11) $x^2 + 2x - 24 =$

12) $x^2 - 3x - 40 =$

13) $x^2 - 3x - 70 =$

14) $x^2 + 26x + 169 =$

15) $4x^2 - 7x - 15 =$

16) $x^2 - 14x + 33 =$

17) $10x^2 + 5x - 15 =$

18) $6x^2 - 4x - 42 =$

19) $x^2 + 12x + 36 =$

20) $5x^2 + 17x - 12 =$

✎ **Calculate each problem.**

21) The area of a rectangle is $x^2 - x - 56$. If the width of rectangle is $x + 7$, what is its length? _____

22) The area of a parallelogram is $4x^2 + 17x - 15$ and its height is $x + 5$. What is the base of the parallelogram? _____

23) The area of a rectangle is $6x^2 - 22x + 12$. If the width of the rectangle is $3x - 2$, what is its length? _____

Operations with Polynomials

✎ **Find each product.**

1) $4(5x + 3) =$ _____

2) $8(2x + 6) =$ _____

3) $2(5x - 2) =$ _____

4) $-4(7x - 3) =$ _____

5) $3x^2(9x + 1) =$ _____

6) $4x^6(7x - 9) =$ _____

7) $3x^4(-7x + 3) =$ _____

8) $-8x^4 (5x - 8) =$ _____

9) $7 (x^2 + 5x - 3) =$ _____

10) $9(5x^2 - 7x + 5) =$ _____

11) $3(3x^2 + 3x + 2) =$ _____

12) $5x(3x^2 + 5x + 8) =$ _____

13) $(5x + 7)(3x - 3) =$ _____

14) $(9x + 3)(3x - 5) =$ _____

15) $(6x + 3)(4x - 2) =$ _____

16) $(7x - 2)(3x + 5) =$ _____

✎ **Calculate each problem.**

17) The measures of two sides of a triangle are $(2x + 5y)$ and $(6x - 3y)$. If the perimeter of the triangle is $(13x + 4y)$, what is the measure of the third side? _____

18) The height of a triangle is $(8x + 5)$ and its base is $(4x - 3)$. What is the area of the triangle? _____

19) One side of a square is $(6x + 2)$. What is the area of the square? _____

20) The length of a rectangle is $(5x - 8y)$ and its width is $(15x + 8y)$. What is the perimeter of the rectangle? _____

21) The side of a cube measures $(x + 2)$. What is the volume of the cube? _____

22) If the perimeter of a rectangle is $(28x + 6y)$ and its width is $(5x + 2y)$, what is the length of the rectangle? _____

Answers of Worksheets

GCF of Monomials

1) $2x$
2) $8a$
3) $15x^3$
4) $12x^4$
5) $10a^2$
6) $10a^2$
7) $8x^2$
8) $11x$
9) 6
10) $15v$

11) pq
12) $6m^3n$
13) $5xy$
14) $22m^2n^2$
15) $7x^3$
16) $2ab^3$
17) $5t^2u^2$
18) $16t$
19) $14r^3$
20) $20ab$

21) 6
22) $8b$
23) $5db$
24) $21m^2n^2$
25) $4x$
26) $2x^2yz^4$
27) 30
28) $8b$
29) $5x$
30) $10a$

Factoring Quadratics

1) $(x - 5)(x - 8)$
2) $(m - 2)(m - 9)$
3) $(p + 8)(p - 6)$
4) $(3b + 5)(b + 8)$
5) $(a - 1)(a - 3)$
6) $(a - 2)(a - 5)$
7) $(5n - 8)(n - 4)$
8) $(t - 7)(t - 4)$
9) $x(4x - 3)(x - 6)$
10) $(x - 3)(x - 7)$
11) $(7r - 9)(r - 4)$
12) $b(4n - 5)(n - 8)$
13) $(3x - 8)(x - 12)$
14) $b(b - 3)(b - 9)$
15) $(5m - 3)(m - 9)$
16) $x(2x - 7)(x - 8)$
17) $(x - 6)(x - 7)$
18) $(p - 1)(p - 12)$

19) $(x - 2)(x - 12)$
20) $(8x - 3)(x - 7)$
21) $(4n - 5)(3n + 2)$
22) $-(3x + 7)(x + 7)$
23) $-(4x + 3)(2x - 1)$
24) $(2x + 9)(3x - 7)$
25) $4(x - 5)(3x - 2)$
26) $(7x - 6)(x - 6)$
27) $4(2n + 3)(n + 8)$
28) $(5x - 3)(x - 3)$
29) $5x(x - 7y)$
30) $-2x(5x + 2y)(x + 12y)$
31) $(4a + 5b)(4a - 3b)$
32) $(5x + 2y)(5x - 4y)$
33) $2y(8x - 9y)(4x - 5y)$
34) $3(x - 7y)(x + 3y)$
35) $7mp(8p - 7)$
36) $3(9b + 5)(b + 5)$

37) $6(2x + 9y)(x + 3y)$

38) $2x(8x + 7y)$

Factoring by Grouping

1) $(6x + k)(3y - 4)$

11) $(2p^2 - 5)(3p + 4)$

2) $(2x + n)(6y - 5)$

12) $(2m - n^2)(9c + 4d)$

3) $(5n^2 + 2)(3n + 2)$

13) $8x(2x^2 - 5)(x + 2)$

4) $3u(3u - 2m)(v + 4u^2)$

14) $(2x + 3y)(4w + 5k)$

5) $4n(2n^2 + 3)(3n + 1)$

15) $(5x + 3r)(5y - 2)$

6) $4(2u + 3b)(2v - u)$

16) $(3x - 7)(y - 2)$

7) $(2x^2 + 9)(x + 3)$

17) $(5x^2 + 2)(x - 8)$

8) $4(x^2 + 2)(x + 4)$

18) $3(6x^2 + 1)(x - 7)$

9) $3(m^2 + 2)(m - 1)$

19) $(3x^2 + 5)(2x + 7)$

10) $3(x^2 - 6)(x - 3)$

20) $6(2x^2 - 5)(x + 3)$

GCF and Powers of monomials

1) $9x^4$

14) $12a^2 b^5$

27) $1,000n^3x^{18}$

2) $22y$

15) 1

28) $4,096x^6y^{24}$

3) 6

16) abc

29) $512x^{12}y^6$

4) $5a$

17) $5ab$

30) $196y^{14}$

5) pq

18) $16m^3 n^4$

31) $625x^{28}$

6) $5 m^2n$

19) $3x$

32) $144x^{20}k^6$

7) $5y$

20) x^2yz^3

33) $27y^{24}$

8) $8 m^2n^2$

21) $8x^{15}$

34) $16,384x^{35}$

9) $9x^2$

22) $216y^{18}$

35) $64y^{12}$

10) $6cb^2$

23) $144y^{12}$

36) $16x^{36}$

11) $5 t^2u^6$

24) $625x^8y^{16}$

37) $1,296y^{36}$

12) $17t$

25) $1,024y^{25}$

38) $625x^4y^{20}$

13) $19 r^2t$

26) $2,187x^{14}y^7$

Writing Polynomials in Standard Form

1) $4x$

4) $14x^4$

2) -5

5) $-9x^3 + 5x^2 + 4x$

3) $6x^5 - 12x^3$

6) $12x^5 - 3x^2$

7) $-2x^8 + 8x^3 + 5x$

8) $-9x^6 - 7x^3 + 4x$

9) $3x^2 - 6x + 22$

10) $9x^4 - 4x + 3$

11) $-8x^3 + 13x^2 + 28x$

12) $-2x^3 + 4x^2 + 16$

13) $9x^4 + 19x^2 - 9x$

14) $3x^4 - 2x^3 - 7x^2$

15) $-8x^4 + 3x^2 - 51$

16) $-8x^6 + 4x^4 + 7x^2 - 15$

17) $-4x^5 + 6x^4 - 3x^3 + 16$

18) $-2x^6 - 7x^2 - x$

19) $6x^7 + 8x^5 - 3x^2$

20) $3x^6 - 12x^5 + 10x^2$

21) $-11x^7 + 20x^5 - 6x^3$

22) $-5x^5 + 34x^4 + 6x^3$

23) $-6x^3 + 12x^2 + 15x$

24) $12x^7 + 48x^4$

25) $15x^3 + 30x^2 + 20x$

26) $42x^6 - 14x^2 + 28x$

27) $12x^5 - 12x^4 + 6x$

28) $8x^6 + 24x^3 - 12x$

29) $15x^5 + 20x^4 + 10x^2$

30) $8x^7 - 4x^4 + 6x^2$

Simplifying Polynomials

1) $12x - 60$

2) $15x^2 - 20x$

3) $30x^2 - 42x$

4) $21x^2 + 15x$

5) $20x^2 - 15x$

6) $48x^2 + 12x$

7) $3x^2 - 14x + 8$

8) $2x^2 - 4x - 30$

9) $x^2 - 10x + 21$

10) $9x^2 - 16$

11) $25x^2 - 30x + 8$

12) $-8x^4 + 12x^2$

13) $5x^3 - 2x^2 + 3x + 7$

14) $-10x^3 + 4x^2 + 7x$

15) $5x^5 - 6x^3 + 12x^2$

16) $6x^8 + 4x^6 - 5x^2$

17) $-4x^6 + 10x^5 - 12x^3 + 4x$

18) $-16x^3 - 3x^2 + 22$

19) $4x^3 + 2x^2 - 4x$

20) $-x^5 - 4x^2 + 18$

21) $x^6 - 14x^3$

22) $12x^4 - 4$

23) $-9x^4 - 12x^3$

24) -90

25) $-9x^4 - 2x + 19$

26) $-7x^5 - 2x^3 + 17$

27) $11x^3 - 10x + 2$

28) $-8x^4 + 2x^2$

29) $2x^5 + 6x + 2$

30) $11x^5 - 5x^4 + 4$

31) $-9x^5 - 28$

32) $9x^3 - 6x$

ALEKS Subject Test Mathematics

Adding and Subtracting Polynomials

1) $x^2 + 1$

2) $6x^3 - 1$

3) $2x^5 + 5x^2 - 15$

4) $6x^3 + 3x^2 - 4x$

5) $-24x^4 + 28x - 6$

6) $14x^2$

7) $14x^2 - 6$

8) $6x^2 - 4$

9) $-3x^3 + 2x$

10) $3x$

11) $19x^3 - 6x$

12) $-7x^5 - 4x$

13) $-11x^7 + 2x^2 + 6x$

14) $4x^5 + 11x^2 - 5$

15) $4x^5 + 18x^4$

16) $-9x^3 + 7x$

17) $-151x^2 + 3x$

18) $-11x^4 + 4x^2 + 5x$

19) $10x^4 - 3x^2 - 4$

20) $10x^6 + 6x^3$

21) $28x^5 + 17x^4 + 22x^2$

22) $10x^4 - 12x$

23) $32x^4 + 4x$

24) $5x^8 - 15x^6 - 5x^3 + 3x$

25) $6x^4 + 15x^2 - 12x$

26) $-2x^9 + 13x^7 + 40x^3$

Multiplying Monomials

1) $-6u^{10}$

2) $10p^{11}$

3) $12xy^3z^9$

4) $24u^6t^5$

5) $35a^5b^6$

6) $-18a^6b^4$

7) $13x^5y^9$

8) $-48p^5q^9$

9) $32s^5t^6$

10) $-36x^6y^4$

11) $36xy^7z^4$

12) $24px^3y^2$

13) $-39p^3q^5$

14) $13s^4t^8$

15) $-66p^8$

16) $-24p^4q^9r^7$

17) $28a^7b$

18) $-30u^9v^6$

19) $-27u^6$

20) $-24x^3y^6$

21) $-13y^8z^4$

22) $16a^5b^2c^6$

23) $35p^9q^8$

24) $-16u^{12}v^6$

25) $-17y^{10}z^6$

26) $-40p^3q^7r^3$

27) $15a^5b^6c^8$

28) $18x^5y^8z^5$

Multiplying and Dividing Monomials

1) $10x^7$

2) $24x^6$

3) $21x^8$

4) $20x^8$

5) $36x^{10}$

6) $32x^{11}y^5$

7) $14x^7y^6$

8) $-10x^6y^9$

9) $18x^7y^7$

10) $-25x^5y^4$

11) $24x^7y^7$

12) $20x^5y^6$

13) $48x^7y^{16}$

14) $45x^7y^{11}$

15) $56x^8y^{14}$

16) $-21x^{12}y^{12}$

17) $5x^5y^2$

18) xy^4

19) $7x^3y^3$

20) $9xy$

21) $4x^5y^3$

22) $12x^5y$

23) $8x^{10}y^3$

24) $5x^{-1}y^3$

25) $5x^3$ 26) $-7x^{14}y^5$ 27) $-4x^2$

Multiplying a Polynomial and a Monomial

1) $2x^2 + 4x$
2) $-12x + 24$
3) $20x^2 + 10x$
4) $-4x^2 + 5x$
5) $16x^2 - 16x$
6) $12x - 24y$
7) $35x^2 - 35x$
8) $36x^2 + 6xy$
9) $4x^2 + 24xy$
10) $33x^2 + 44xy$
11) $21x^2 + 14x$
12) $40x^2 - 100xy$
13) $27x^2 - 18xy$
14) $7x^2 - 28xy + 42x$
15) $16x^3 + 40xy^2$
16) $24x^2 + 36xy$

17) $8x^4 - 16y^4$
18) $-12x^3y + 16xy$
19) $-20x^3 + 8xy - 16$
20) $4x^2 - 20xy - 24$
21) $16x^4 - 40x^2y + 16x^2$
22) $12x^4 + 36x^2 - 12x^2y$
23) $6x^2 + 3xy - 27y^2$
24) $20x^4 - 12x^2 + 28x$
25) $18x^{22} - 12x - 30$
26) $-2x^5 + 4x^3 + 3x^2$
27) $4x^5 - 2x^3 + 10x^2$
28) $12x^7 - 8x^5 + 20x^4$
29) $8x^6 - 10x^3y + 14x^2y^3$
30) $25x^6 - 15x^3 + 45x^2$
31) $42x^4 + 21x^3 - 42x^2$
32) $4x^4 - 16x^2y + 8xy^2$

Multiplying Binomials

1) $x^2 + 9x + 18$
2) $x^2 - x - 12$
3) $x^2 - 11x + 24$
4) $x^2 + 17x + 72$
5) $x^2 - 14x + 24$
6) $x^2 + 10x + 25$
7) $x^2 + x - 42$
8) $x^2 - 11x + 24$
9) $x^2 + 19x + 84$
10) $x^2 + 4x - 32$
11) $x^2 + 16x + 64$

12) $x^2 + 9x + 14$
13) $x^2 - 36$
14) $x^2 - 25$
15) $x^2 + 22x + 121$
16) $x^2 + 15x + 54$
17) $x^2 - 4$
18) $x^2 + 3x - 28$
19) $3x^2 + 23x + 30$
20) $20x^2 + 16x - 48$
21) $3x^2 - 14x - 49$
22) $x^2 - 13x + 36$

23) $x^2 - 10x - 24$

24) $10x^2 - 12x - 16$

25) $3x^2 + 16x - 64$

26) $42x^2 + 9x - 6$

27) $12x^2 + 35x + 25$

28) $63x^2 - 8x - 16$

29) $2x^2 - 4x - 16$

30) $25x^2 - 16$

31) $9x^2 - 15x - 14$

32) $x^4 - 64$

Factoring Trinomials

1) $(x + 6)(x + 2)$

2) $(x - 5)(x - 1)$

3) $(x + 12)(x + 3)$

4) $(x - 5)(x - 7)$

5) $(x - 2)(x - 9)$

6) $(x - 6)(x - 3)$

7) $(x + 6)(x + 12)$

8) $(x + 8)(x - 9)$

9) $(x - 3)(x + 7)$

10) $(x - 11)(x - 2)$

11) $(x - 4)(x + 6)$

12) $(x - 8)(x + 5)$

13) $(x + 7)(x - 10)$

14) $(x + 13)(x + 13)$

15) $(4x + 5)(x - 3)$

16) $(x - 11)(x - 3)$

17) $(5x - 5)(2x + 3)$

18) $(2x - 6)(3x + 7)$

19) $(x + 6)(x + 6)$

20) $(5x - 3)(x + 4)$

21) $(x - 8)$

22) $(4x - 3)$

23) $(2x - 6)$

Operations with Polynomials

1) $20x + 12$

2) $16x + 48$

3) $10x - 4$

4) $-28x + 12$

5) $27x^3 + 3x^2$

6) $28x^7 - 36x^6$

7) $-21x^5 + 9x^4$

8) $-40x^5 + 64x^4$

9) $7x^2 + 35x - 21$

10) $45x^2 - 63x + 45$

11) $9x^2 + 9x + 6$

12) $15x^3 + 25x^2 + 40x$

13) $15x^2 + 6x - 21$

14) $27x^2 - 36x - 15$

15) $24x^2 - 6$

16) $21x^2 + 29x - 10$

17) $(5x + 2y)$

18) $16x^2 - 2x - \frac{15}{2}$

19) $36x^2 + 24x + 4$

20) $40x$

21) $x^3 + 6x^2 + 12x + 8$

22) $(9x + y)$

Chapter 10 :

Functions Operations and Quadratic

Topics that you'll practice in this chapter:

- ✓ Relations and Functions
- ✓ Evaluating Function
- ✓ Adding and Subtracting Functions
- ✓ Multiplying and Dividing Functions
- ✓ Composition of Functions
- ✓ Quadratic Equation
- ✓ Solving Quadratic Equations
- ✓ Quadratic Formula and the Discriminant
- ✓ Quadratic Inequalities
- ✓ Graphing Quadratic Functions
- ✓ Domain and Range of Radical Functions
- ✓ Solving Radical Equations

It's fine to work on any problem, so long as it generates interesting mathematics along the way – even if you don't solve it at the end of the day." – Andrew Wiles

Relations and Functions

✎ **State the domain and range of each relation. Then determine whether each relation is a function.**

1)

Function:

....

Domain:

....

Range:

....

```
   ┌─────┐      ┌─────┐
   │  1  │─────▶│  3  │
   │  3  │─────▶│  5  │
   │  5  │─────▶│  8  │
   │  7  │─────▶│ 12  │
   │  9  │─────▶│ 18  │
   └─────┘      └─────┘
```

2)

Function:

....

Domain:

....

Range:

....

x	y
3	4
0	1
−2	−3
6	−3
8	2

3)

Function:

....

Domain:

....

Range:

....

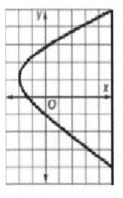

4) $\{(1, -2), (4, -1), (0, 5), (4, 0), (3, 8)\}$

Function:

....

Domain:

....

Range:

....

5)

Function:

....

Domain:

....

Range:

....

6)

Function:

....

Domain:

....

Range:

....

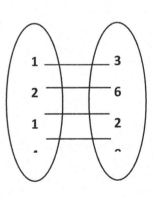

Evaluating Function

✍ **Write each of following in function notation.**

1) $h = -8x + 3$

2) $k = 2a - 14$

3) $d = 11t$

4) $y = \frac{5}{12}x - \frac{7}{12}$

5) $m = 24n - 210$

6) $c = p^2 - 5p + 10$

✍ **Evaluate each function.**

7) $f(x) = 2x - 7$, find $f(-3)$

8) $g(x) = \frac{1}{9}x + 12$, find $f(18)$

9) $h(x) = -4x + 9$, find $f(3)$

10) $f(x) = -x + 19$, find $f(-3)$

11) $f(a) = 7a - 12$, find $f(3)$

12) $h(x) = 14 - 3x$, find $f(-4)$

13) $g(n) = 6n - 10$, find $f(2)$

14) $f(x) = -11x - 4$, find $f(-1)$

15) $k(n) = -20 - 3.5n$, find $f(2)$

16) $f(x) = -0.7x + 3.3$, find $f(-7)$

17) $g(n) = \frac{11n+8}{n}$, find $g(2)$

18) $g(n) = \sqrt{3n} + 12$, find $g(3)$

19) $h(x) = x^{-2} - 7$, find $h(\frac{1}{9})$

20) $h(n) = n^{-3} + 11$, find $h(\frac{1}{4})$

21) $h(n) = n^3 - 2$, find $h(\frac{1}{2})$

22) $h(n) = n^2 - 4$, find $h(-\frac{1}{3})$

23) $h(n) = 4n^2 - 13$, find $h(-5)$

24) $h(n) = -2n^3 - 6n$, find $h(2)$

25) $g(n) = \sqrt{16n^2} - \sqrt{n}$, find $g(4)$

26) $h(a) = \frac{-14a+9}{3a}$, find $h(-b)$

27) $k(a) = 12a - 14$, find $k(a - 3)$

28) $h(x) = \frac{1}{9}x + 18$, find $h(-18x)$

29) $h(x) = 8x^2 + 16$, find $h(\frac{x}{2})$

30) $h(x) = x^4 - 20$, find $h(-2x)$

Adding and Subtracting Functions

✎ **Perform the indicated operation.**

1) $f(x) = 2x + 3$

   $g(x) = x + 7$

   Find $(f - g)(2)$

2) $g(a) = -5a - 8$

   $f(a) = -3a - 5$

   Find $(g - f)(-2)$

3) $h(t) = 4t + 3$

   $g(t) = 4t + 7$

   Find $(h - g)(t)$

4) $g(a) = -6a - 10$

   $f(a) = 3a^2 + 9$

   Find $(g - f)(x)$

5) $g(x) = \frac{5}{6}x - 23$

   $h(x) = \frac{5}{12}x + 25$

   Find $g(12) - h(12)$

6) $h(x) = \sqrt{3x} - 2$

   $g(x) = \sqrt{3x} + 5$

   Find $(h + g)(12)$

7) $f(x) = x^{-1}$

   $g(x) = x^2 + \frac{5}{x}$

   Find $(f - g)(-3)$

8) $h(n) = n^2 + 2$

   $g(n) = -4n + 6$

   Find $(h - g)(2a)$

9) $g(x) = -2x^2 - 5 - 4x$

   $f(x) = 7 + 2x$

   Find $(g - f)(3x)$

10) $g(t) = 11t - 4$

    $f(t) = -2t^2 + 5$

    Find $(g + f)(-t)$

11) $f(x) = 8x + 9$

    $g(x) = -5x^2 + 3x$

    Find $(f - g)(-x^2)$

12) $f(x) = -3x^4 - 5x$

    $g(x) = 2x^4 + 5x + 22$

    Find $(f + g)(3x^2)$

Multiplying and Dividing Functions

✎ **Perform the indicated operation.**

1) $g(x) = -2x - 1$

$f(x) = 4x + 3$

Find $(g.f)(2)$

2) $f(x) = 5x$

$h(x) = -2x + 3$

Find $(f.h)(-2)$

3) $g(a) = 5a - 2$

$h(a) = 2a - 3$

Find $(g.h)(-3)$

4) $f(x) = 2x - 7$

$h(x) = x - 5$

Find $(\frac{f}{h})(4)$

5) $f(x) = 8a^2$

$g(x) = 3 + 2a$

Find $(\frac{f}{g})(2)$

6) $g(a) = \sqrt{4a} + 2$

$f(a) = (-a)^4 + 1$

Find $(\frac{g}{f})(1)$

7) $g(t) = t^3 + 1$

$h(t) = 5t - 2$

Find $(g.h)(-2)$

8) $g(n) = n^2 + 2n - 4$

$h(n) = -5n + 3$

Find $(g.h)(1)$

9) $g(a) = (a - 3)^2$

$f(a) = a^2 + 4$

Find $(\frac{g}{f})(3)$

10) $g(x) = -3x^2 + \frac{4}{5}x + 9$

$f(x) = x^2 - 24$

Find $(\frac{g}{f})(5)$

11) $f(x) = 2x^3 - 5x^2 + 1$

$g(x) = 3x - 1$

Find $(f.g)(x)$

12) $f(x) = 5x - 2$

$g(x) = x^3 - 2x$

Find $(f.g)(x^2)$

Composition of Functions

✎ Using $f(x) = 2x - 5$ and $g(x) = -2x$, find:

1) $f(g(2)) =$

2) $f(g(-1)) =$

3) $g(f(-4)) =$

4) $g(f(5)) =$

5) $f(g(3)) =$

6) $g(f(0)) =$

✎ Using $f(x) = -\frac{1}{4}x + \frac{3}{4}$ and $g(x) = 2x^2$, find:

7) $g(f(-2)) =$

8) $g(f(4)) =$

9) $g(g(1)) =$

10) $f(f(1)) =$

11) $g(f(-4)) =$

12) $f(g(x)) =$

✎ Using $f(x) = -2x + 2$ and $g(x) = x + 1$, find:

13) $g(f(1)) =$

14) $f(f(0)) =$

15) $f(g(-1)) =$

16) $f(g(-3)) =$

17) $g(f(2)) =$

18) $f(g(x)) =$

✎ Using $f(x) = \sqrt{x + 9}$ and $g(x) = x - 9$, find:

19) $f(g(9)) =$

20) $g(f(-9)) =$

21) $f(g(4)) =$

22) $f(f(7)) =$

23) $g(f(-5)) =$

24) $g(g(0)) =$

Quadratic Equation

✍ Multiply.

1) $(x - 4)(x + 6) =$ _____

2) $(x + 5)(x + 7) =$ _____

3) $(x - 6)(x + 8) =$ _____

4) $(x + 2)(x - 9) =$ _____

5) $(x - 7)(x - 8) =$ _____

6) $(3x + 2)(x - 3) =$ _____

7) $(4x - 3)(x + 2) =$ _____

8) $(4x - 5)(x + 1) =$ _____

9) $(7x + 1)(x - 6) =$ _____

10) $(5x + 1)(3x - 3) =$ _____

✍ Factor each expression.

11) $x^2 - 2x - 8 =$ _____

12) $x^2 + 8x + 15 =$ _____

13) $x^2 - 2x - 24 =$ _____

14) $x^2 - 10x + 21 =$ _____

15) $x^2 + 10x + 21 =$ _____

16) $4x^2 + 9x + 5 =$ _____

17) $5x^2 + 13x - 6 =$ _____

18) $5x^2 + 17x - 12 =$ _____

19) $2x^2 + 7x + 5 =$ _____

20) $9x^2 - 21x + 6 =$ _____

✍ Calculate each equation.

21) $(x + 6)(x - 3) = 0$

22) $(x + 1)(x + 8) = 0$

23) $(3x + 6)(x + 5) = 0$

24) $(2x - 2)(4x + 8) = 0$

25) $x^2 + x + 10 = 22$

26) $x^2 + 11x + 36 = 12$

27) $2x^2 + 9x + 9 = 5$

28) $x^2 + 3x - 24 = 4$

29) $5x^2 + 5x - 40 = 20$

30) $8x^2 + 8x = 48$

Solving Quadratic Equations

✎ **Solve each equation by factoring or using the quadratic formula.**

1) $(x + 9)(x - 1) = 0$

2) $(x + 7)(x + 6) = 0$

3) $(x - 8)(x + 3) = 0$

4) $(x - 6)(x - 4) = 0$

5) $(x + 2)(x + 12) = 0$

6) $(5x + 4)(x + 7) = 0$

7) $(6x + 1)(4x + 5) = 0$

8) $(2x + 7)(x + 8) = 0$

9) $(x + 6)(3x + 15) = 0$

10) $(12x + 2)(x + 8) = 0$

11) $x^2 = 8x$

12) $x^2 - 16 = 0$

13) $3x^2 + 6 = 9x$

14) $-2x^2 - 8 = 10x$

15) $5x^2 + 40x = 45$

16) $x^2 + 10x = 24$

17) $x^2 + 6x = 16$

18) $x^2 + 9x = -18$

19) $x^2 + 13x = -36$

20) $x^2 + 3x - 15 = 5x$

21) $x^2 + 8x + 7 = -8$

22) $3x^2 - 11x = -9 + x$

23) $10x^2 + 3 = 27x - 15$

24) $7x^2 - 6x + 8 = 8$

25) $2x^2 - 12 = -3x + 2$

26) $10x^2 - 26x - 3 = -15$

27) $3x^2 + 21 = -16x + 5$

28) $x^2 + 15x - 10 = -66$

29) $3x^2 - 8x - 8 = 4 + x$

30) $2x^2 + 6x - 24 = 12$

31) $3x^2 - 33x + 54 = -18$

32) $-10x^2 - 15x - 9 = -9 - 27x^2$

Quadratic Formula and the Discriminant

✎ Find the value of the discriminant of each quadratic equation.

1) $3x(x - 8) = 0$

2) $2x^2 + 6x - 4 = 0$

3) $x^2 + 6x + 7 = 0$

4) $x^2 - x + 3 = 0$

5) $x^2 + 4x - 3 = 0$

6) $2x^2 + 6x - 10 = 0$

7) $3x^2 + 7x + 5 = 0$

8) $x^2 - 6x - 4 = 0$

9) $2x^2 + 8x + 3 = 0$

10) $x^2 + 7x - 5 = 0$

11) $5x^2 + 2x - 3 = 0$

12) $-3x^2 - 11x + 4 = 0$

13) $-6x^2 - 12x + 8 = 0$

14) $-x^2 - 9x - 12 = 0$

15) $7x^2 - 6x - 10 = 0$

16) $-4x^2 - 2x + 8 = 0$

17) $5x^2 + 8x - 2 = 0$

18) $6x^2 - 4x = 0$

19) $3x^2 - 5x + 2 = 0$

20) $4x^2 + 9x + 3 = 0$

✎ Find the discriminant of each quadratic equation then state the number of real and imaginary solutions.

21) $-4x^2 - 16 = 16x$

22) $20x^2 = 20x - 5$

23) $-11x^2 - 19x = 26$

24) $22x^2 - 4x + 1 = 18x^2$

25) $-11x^2 = -15x + 8$

26) $3x^2 + 6x + 9 = 6$

27) $13x^2 - 5x - 12 = -26$

28) $-8x^2 - 32x - 25 = 7$

Graphing Quadratic Functions

✍ketch the graph of each function. Identify the vertex and axis of symmetry.

1) $y = (x + 3)^2 + 2$

2) $y = (x - 3)^2 - 2$

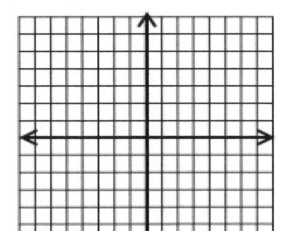
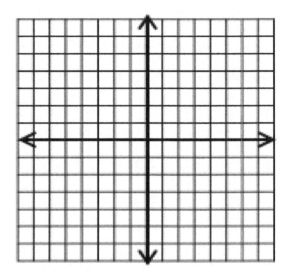

3) $y = 6 - (-x + 4)^2$

4) $y = -3x^2 - 6x + 9$

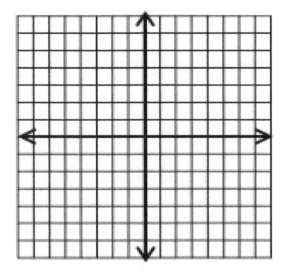
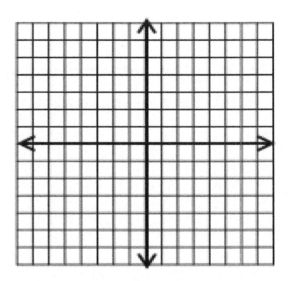

Quadratic Inequalities

✎Solve each quadratic inequality.

1) $x^2 - 25 < 0$

2) $-x^2 - 6x - 8 > 0$

3) $5x^2 + 15x + 30 < 0$

4) $x^2 + 8x + 16 > 0$

5) $2x^2 - 18x - 20 \geq 0$

6) $x^2 > -10x - 25$

7) $3x^2 + 2x + 16 \leq 0$

8) $x^2 - 5x - 14 \leq 0$

9) $x^2 - 6x - 7 \geq 0$

10) $2x^2 + 16x - 18 < 0$

11) $x^2 + 6x - 72 > 0$

12) $3x^2 - 3x - 36 > 0$

13) $x^2 - 15x + 64 \leq 0$

14) $2x^2 - 24x + 72 \leq 0$

15) $x^2 - 16x + 63 \geq 0$

16) $x^2 - 16x + 55 \geq 0$

17) $x^2 - 81 \leq 0$

18) $x^2 - 17x + 42 \geq 0$

19) $9x^2 + 14x + 36 \leq 0$

20) $4x^2 - 2x - 24 > 2x^2$

21) $5x^2 - 20x + 20 < 0$

22) $7x^2 - 6x \geq 6x^2 - 5$

23) $5x^2 - 15 > 4x^2 + 2x$

24) $3x^2 - 4x \geq 3x^2 - 9x + 15$

25) $8x^2 + 9x - 54 > 5x^2$

26) $10x^2 + 50x - 60 < 0$

27) $-x^2 + 15x - 57 \geq 0$

28) $-5x^2 + 25x + 30 \leq 0$

29) $5x^2 + 40x + 75 < 0$

30) $9x^2 + 20x + 180 \leq 0$

31) $3x^2 + 2x - 36 \geq -x$

32) $3x^2 + 9x + 9 \leq 6x^2 + 3x$

Domain and Range of Radical Functions

✎ **Identify the domain and range of each function.**

1) $y = \sqrt{x + 8} - 7$

2) $y = \sqrt[3]{3x - 5} - 4$

3) $y = \sqrt{3x - 9} + 3$

4) $y = \sqrt[3]{(4x + 6)} - 2$

5) $y = 3\sqrt{4x + 20} + 6$

6) $y = \sqrt[3]{(5x - 2)} - 11$

7) $y = 4\sqrt{9x^2 + 8} + 3$

8) $y = \sqrt[3]{(7x^2 - 2)} - 6$

9) $y = 2\sqrt{2x^3 + 16} - 3$

10) $y = \sqrt[3]{(11x + 4)} - 2x$

11) $y = 3\sqrt{-2(4x + 8)} + 5$

12) $y = \sqrt[5]{(3x^2 - 12)} - 6$

13) $y = 3\sqrt{x - 5} - 2$

14) $y = \sqrt[3]{6x + 9} - 4$

✎ **Sketch the graph of each function.**

15) $y = -3\sqrt{x} + 5$

16) $y = 3\sqrt{x} - 6$

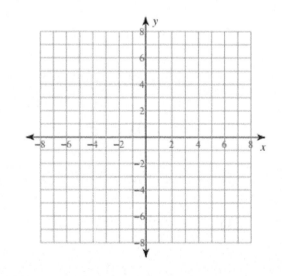

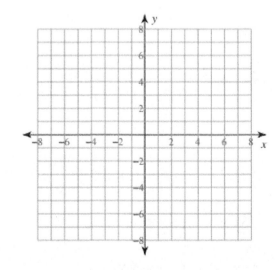

Solving Radical Equations

✎ Solve each equation. Remember to check for extraneous solutions.

1) $\sqrt{a} = 9$

2) $\sqrt{v} = 6$

3) $\sqrt{r} = 4$

4) $8 = 16\sqrt{x}$

5) $\sqrt{x+3} = 18$

6) $6 = \sqrt{x-7}$

7) $4 = \sqrt{r-3}$

8) $\sqrt{x-5} = 7$

9) $12 = \sqrt{x-4}$

10) $\sqrt{m+5} = 8$

11) $7\sqrt{5a} = 35$

12) $6\sqrt{2x} = 48$

13) $2 = \sqrt{6x-32}$

14) $\sqrt{304-4x} = 4$

15) $\sqrt{r+2} - 8 = 6$

16) $-21 = -7\sqrt{r+9}$

17) $60 = 6\sqrt{5v}$

18) $x = \sqrt{40-3x}$

19) $\sqrt{90-27a} = 3a$

20) $\sqrt{-8n+88} = 4$

21) $\sqrt{15r-5} = 4r-3$

22) $\sqrt{-64+32x} = 4x$

23) $\sqrt{4x+15} = \sqrt{2x+11}$

24) $\sqrt{12v} = \sqrt{15v-21}$

25) $\sqrt{9-x} = \sqrt{x-3}$

26) $\sqrt{6m+34} = \sqrt{8m+34}$

27) $\sqrt{7r+32} = \sqrt{-8-3r}$

28) $\sqrt{4k+10} = \sqrt{2-4k}$

29) $-20\sqrt{x-13} = -40$

30) $\sqrt{90-2x} = \sqrt{\dfrac{x}{4}}$

Answers of Worksheets

Relation and Functions

1) No, $D_f = \{1, 3, 5, 7, 9\}$, $R_f = \{3, 5, 8, 12, 18\}$

2) Yes, $D_f = \{3, 0, -2, 6, 8\}$, $R_f = \{4, 1, -3, 2\}$

3) Yes, $D_f = (-\infty, \infty)$, $R_f = \{2, -\infty)$

4) No, $D_f = \{1, 4, 0, 3\}$, $R_f = \{-2, -1, 5, 0, 8\}$

5) No, $D_f = [-2, \infty)$, $R_f = (-\infty, \infty)$

6) No, $D_f = \{1, 2, 4\}$, $R_f = \{3, 6, 2, 8\}$

Evaluating Function

1) $h(x) = -8x + 3$

2) $k(a) = 2a - 14$

3) $d(t) = 11t$

4) $f(x) = \frac{5}{12}x - \frac{7}{12}$

5) $m(n) = 24n - 210$

6) $c(p) = p^2 - 5p + 10$

7) -13

8) 14

9) -3

10) 22

11) 9

12) 26

13) 2

14) 7

15) -27

16) 8.2

17) 15

18) 15

19) 74

20) 75

21) $-1\frac{7}{8}$

22) $-3\frac{8}{9}$

23) 87

24) -28

25) 14

26) $-\frac{14b+9}{3b}$

27) $12a - 50$

28) $-2x + 18$

29) $2x^2 + 16$

30) $16x^4 - 20$

Adding and Subtracting Functions

1) -2

2) 1

3) -4

4) $-3x^2 - 6x - 19$

5) -43

6) 15

7) $-7\frac{2}{3}$

8) $4a^2 + 8a - 4$

9) $-18x^2 - 18x - 12$

10) $-2t^2 - 11t + 1$

11) $5x^4 - 5x^2 + 9$

12) $-81x^8 + 22$

Multiplying and Dividing Functions

1) -55

2) -70

3) 153

4) -1

5) $4\frac{4}{7}$

6) 2

7) 84

8) 2

9) 0

10) -62

11) $6x^4 - 17x^3 + 5x^2 + 3x - 1$ 12) $5x^8 - 2x^6 - 10x^4 + 4x^2$

Composition of Functions

1) -13

2) -1

3) 26

4) -10

5) -17

6) 10

7) $\frac{25}{8}$

8) $\frac{1}{8}$

9) 8

10) $\frac{5}{8}$

11) $\frac{49}{8}$

12) $-\frac{1}{2}(x^2 - \frac{3}{2})$

13) 1

14) -2

15) 2

16) 6

17) -1

18) $-2x$

19) 3

20) -9

21) 2

22) $\sqrt{13}$

23) -7

24) -18

Quadratic Equations

1) $x^2 + 2x - 24$

2) $x^2 + 12x + 35$

3) $x^2 + 2x - 48$

4) $x^2 - 7x - 18$

5) $x^2 - 15x + 56$

6) $3x^2 - 7x - 6$

7) $4x^2 + 5x - 6$

8) $4x^2 - x - 5$

9) $7x^2 - 41x - 6$

10) $15x^2 - 12x - 3$

11) $(x - 4)(x + 2)$

12) $(x + 5)(x + 3)$

13) $(x - 6)(x + 4)$

14) $(x - 3)(x - 7)$

15) $(x + 3)(x + 7)$

16) $(4x + 5)(x + 1)$

17) $(5x - 2)(x + 3)$

18) $(5x - 3)(x + 4)$

19) $(2x + 5)(x + 1)$

20) $3(x - 2)(3x - 1)$

21) $x = -6, x = 3$

22) $x = -1, x = -8$

23) $x = -2, x = -5$

24) $x = 1, x = -2$

25) $x = 3, x = -4$

26) $x = -3, x = -8$

27) $x = -4, x = -\frac{1}{2}$

28) $x = 4, x = -7$

29) $x = 3, x = -4$

30) $x = -3, x = 2$

Solving quadratic equations

1) $\{-9, 1\}$

2) $\{-6, -7\}$

3) $\{8, -3\}$

4) $\{6, 4\}$

5) $\{-2, -12\}$

6) $\{-\frac{4}{5}, -7\}$

7) $\{-\frac{5}{4}, -\frac{1}{6}\}$

8) $\{-\frac{7}{2}, -8\}$

9) $\{-6, -5\}$

10) $\{-\frac{1}{6}, -8\}$

11) $\{8, 0\}$

12) $\{4, -4\}$

13) $\{2, 1\}$

14) $\{-4, -1\}$

15) $\{1, -9\}$

16) $\{2, -12\}$

17) $\{2, -8\}$

18) $\{-3, -6\}$

19) $\{-4, -9\}$

20) $\{5, -3\}$

21) $\{-5, -3\}$

22) $\{1, 3\}$

23) $\{\frac{6}{5}, \frac{3}{2}\}$

24) $\{\frac{6}{7}, 0\}$

25) $\{-\frac{7}{2}, 2\}$

26) $\{\frac{3}{5}, 2\}$

27) $\{-\frac{4}{3}, -4\}$

28) $\{-8, -7\}$

29) $\{4, -1\}$

30) $\{3, -6\}$

31) $\{3, 8\}$

32) $\{\frac{15}{17}, 0\}$

Quadratic formula and the discriminant

1) 576	6) 116	11) 64	16) 132
2) 68	7) −11	12) 169	17) 104
3) 8	8) 52	13) 336	18) 16
4) −11	9) 40	14) 33	19) 1
5) 28	10) 69	15) 316	20) 33

21) 0, *one real solution*   24) 0, *one real solution*   27) −703, *no solution*

22) 0, *one real solution*   25) −127, *no solution*   28) 0, *one real solution*

23) −783, *no solution*   26) 0, *one real solution*

Graphing quadratic functions

1) $(-3, 2), x = -3$

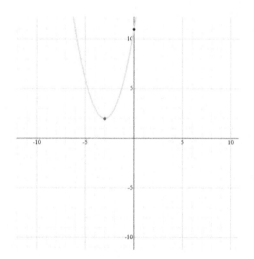

2) $(3, -2), x = 3$

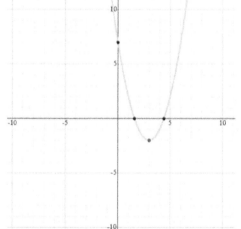

3) $(4, 6), x = 4$

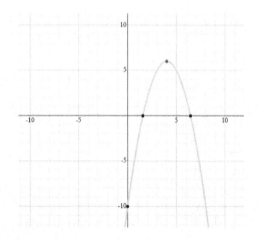

4) $(-1, 12), x = -1$

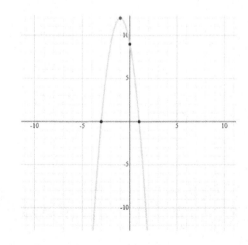

ALEKS Subject Test Mathematics

Quadratic inequalities

1) $-5 < x < 5$

2) $-4 < x < -2$

3) no solution

4) $x < -4 \ or \ x > -4$

5) $x \leq -1 \ or \ x \geq 10$

6) $x < -5 \ or \ x > -5$

7) no solution

8) $-2 \leq x \leq 7$

9) $x \leq -1 \ or \ x \geq 7$

10) $-9 < x < 1$

11) $x < -12 \ or \ x > 6$

12) $-3 < x < 4$

13) no solution

14) $x = 6$

15) $x \leq 7 or \ x \geq 9$

16) $x \leq 5 or \ x \geq 11$

17) $-9 \leq x \leq 9$

18) $x \leq 3 \ or \ x \geq 14$

19) no solution

20) $x < -3 \ or \ x > 4$

21) no solution

22) $x \leq 1 \ or \ x \geq 5$

23) $x < -3 \ or \ x > 5$

24) $x \geq 3$

25) $x < -6 \ or \ x > 3$

26) $-6 < x < 1$

27) no solution

28) $x \leq -1 \ or \ x \geq 6$

29) $-5 < x < -3$

30) no solution

31) $x \leq -4 \ or \ x \geq 3$

32) $x \leq -1 \ or \ x \geq 3$

Domain and range of radical functions

1) domain: $x \geq -8$

   range: $y \geq -7$

2) domain: {all real numbers}

   range: {all real numbers}

3) domain: $x \geq 3$

   range: $y \geq 3$

4) domain: {all real numbers}

   range: {all real numbers}

5) domain: $x \geq -5$

   range: $y \geq 6$

6) domain: {all real numbers}

   range: {all real numbers}

7) domain: {all real numbers}

   range: $y \geq 8\sqrt{2} + 3$

8) domain: {all real numbers}

   range: {all real numbers}

9) domain: $x \geq -2$

   range: $y \geq -3$

10) domain: {all real numbers}

    range: {all real numbers}

11) domain: $x \leq -2$

    range: $y \geq 5$

12) domain: {all real numbers}

    range: {all real numbers}

13) domain: $x \geq 5$

    range: $y \geq -2$

14) domain: {all real numbers}

    range: {all real numbers}

15)

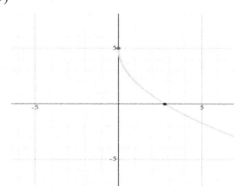

16)

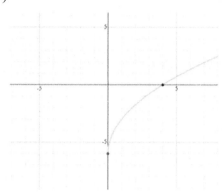

Solving radical equations

1) {81}

2) {36}

3) {16}

4) {$\frac{1}{4}$}

5) {321}

6) {43}

7) {19}

8) {54}

9) {148}

10) {59}

11) {5}

12) {32}

13) {6}

14) {72}

15) {194}

16) {0}

17) {20}

18) {5}

19) {2}

20) {9}

21) {2}

22) no solution

23) {−2}

24) {7}

25) {6}

26) {0}

27) {−4}

28) {−1}

29) {17}

30) {40}

Chapter 11 :

Rational Expressions

Topics that you will learn in this chapter:

✓ Simplifying and Graphing Rational Expressions

✓ Adding and Subtracting Rational Expressions

✓ Multiplying and Dividing Rational Expressions

✓ Solving Rational Equations and Complex Fractions

"What music is to the heart; mathematics is to the mind."
— Amit Kalantri

Simplifying and Graphing Rational Expressions

✎ **Simplify.**

1) $\dfrac{x+3}{3x+9} =$

5) $\dfrac{16x^4}{24x} =$

2) $\dfrac{3x^2+12x+12}{x+2} =$

6) $\dfrac{x-1}{x^2+4x-5} =$

3) $\dfrac{8}{4x-4} =$

7) $\dfrac{x^2-5x-14}{x-7} =$

4) $\dfrac{x^2+6x+5}{x^2+9x+20} =$

8) $\dfrac{36}{6x-6} =$

✎ **Identify the points of discontinuity, holes, vertical asymptotes, x–intercepts, and horizontal asymptote of each.**

9) $f(x) = \dfrac{x^2-x+2}{-4x^2-4x+8} =$

11) $f(x) = \dfrac{x-2}{x-7} =$

10) $f(x) = \dfrac{-x-2}{-3x^2-15x-18} =$

12) $f(x) = \dfrac{3x^2}{3x^2-3x-6} =$

✎ **Graph rational expressions.**

13) $f(x) = \dfrac{-x^2+3x-4}{x-3}$

14) $f(x) = \dfrac{-x^3-10x+32}{x^2-x-3}$

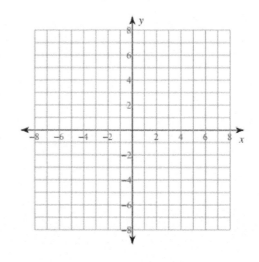

Adding and Subtracting Rational Expressions

✎ **Simplify each expression.**

1) $\dfrac{3}{3x+7} + \dfrac{x-5}{3x+7} =$

2) $\dfrac{x+2}{x-2} + \dfrac{x-2}{x+5} =$

3) $\dfrac{2}{x+3} - \dfrac{5}{x-8} =$

4) $\dfrac{x-3}{x^2-11} - \dfrac{x-4}{11-x^2} =$

5) $\dfrac{2}{x+4} + \dfrac{6x}{3x+12} =$

6) $\dfrac{7+x}{2x} + \dfrac{x-3}{2x} =$

7) $3 + \dfrac{x-4}{x+3} =$

8) $\dfrac{3x}{3x+5} + \dfrac{5x}{4x+1} =$

9) $\dfrac{x+y}{y-x} - \dfrac{2xy}{y^2-x^2} =$

10) $\dfrac{3}{x^2-2x-8} + \dfrac{-3}{x^2-4} =$

11) $\dfrac{3}{x+4} - \dfrac{1}{x+2} =$

12) $\dfrac{4x+4}{4x^2+12x-16} + \dfrac{5x}{3x} =$

13) $2 + \dfrac{x}{x+2} - \dfrac{2}{x^2-4} =$

14) $\dfrac{3}{x+2} - \dfrac{3}{x+5} =$

15) $\dfrac{1}{5x^2+15x} + \dfrac{3}{2x} =$

16) $\dfrac{x^2+4x+4}{4x+8} + \dfrac{3x+3}{x+1} =$

17) $\dfrac{x}{3x+5} + \dfrac{3x}{3x+4} =$

18) $\dfrac{3}{12+4x} - \dfrac{3x-5}{4x^2+12x} =$

Multiplying and Dividing Rational Expressions

✎ **Simplify each expression.**

1) $\dfrac{10x}{15} \times \dfrac{15}{12x} =$

2) $\dfrac{63x}{12} \times \dfrac{60}{28x^2} =$

3) $\dfrac{75}{4} \times \dfrac{24x}{87} =$

4) $\dfrac{58}{27} \times \dfrac{27x^2}{43} =$

5) $\dfrac{90}{14x} \times \dfrac{32x}{45x} =$

6) $\dfrac{6x+30}{x+2} \times \dfrac{x+2}{6} =$

7) $\dfrac{x-9}{x+5} \times \dfrac{8x+40}{x-9} =$

8) $\dfrac{2}{x+11} \times \dfrac{5x+55}{5x+10} =$

9) $\dfrac{4(x+5)}{5x} \times \dfrac{9}{4(x+5)} =$

10) $\dfrac{7(x+3)}{x+3} \times \dfrac{7x}{7(x-5)} =$

11) $\dfrac{5x^2+10x}{x+6} \times \dfrac{1}{x+2} =$

12) $\dfrac{16x^2-16x}{14x^2-14x} \times \dfrac{6x}{6x^2} =$

13) $\dfrac{1}{x-7} \times \dfrac{x^2+4x-21}{x+7} =$

14) $\dfrac{x^2-12x+36}{12x-72} \times \dfrac{x-6}{36-6x} =$

✎ **Divide.**

15) $\dfrac{-1+2x-x^2}{x^2+4x-5} \div \dfrac{3x}{x+5} =$

16) $\dfrac{9a}{a+7} \div \dfrac{9a}{2a+14} =$

17) $\dfrac{13x}{x-9} \div \dfrac{13x}{8x-72} =$

18) $\dfrac{3x+12}{8x^2-80x} \div \dfrac{3}{8x} =$

19) $\dfrac{x-3}{x+3x-12} \div \dfrac{11x}{x+8} =$

20) $\dfrac{6x}{x-8} \div \dfrac{6x}{12x-96} =$

21) $\dfrac{x+6}{x^2+14x+48} \div \dfrac{5x}{x+8} =$

22) $\dfrac{x+2}{x^2+15x+54} \div \dfrac{5x}{x+9} =$

23) $\dfrac{16x+14}{4} \div \dfrac{64x+56}{4x} =$

24) $\dfrac{7x^3+49x^2}{x^2+16x+63} \div \dfrac{4(x+6)}{4x^3+24x^2} =$

25) $\dfrac{x^2+9x+14}{x^2+6x+8} \div \dfrac{1}{x+4} =$

26) $\dfrac{x^2+3x-10}{6x+30} \div \dfrac{3}{x+7} =$

27) $\dfrac{x+6}{x^2+10x+21} \div \dfrac{1}{x+7} =$

28) $\dfrac{1}{4x} \div \dfrac{8x}{2x^2+18x} =$

Solving Rational Equations and Complex Fractions

✍ **Solve each equation. Remember to check for extraneous solutions.**

1) $\dfrac{x-1}{x+3} = \dfrac{2x-2}{x-3}$

2) $\dfrac{1}{x} = \dfrac{5}{6x} + 2$

3) $\dfrac{3x-4}{6x+1} = \dfrac{x+4}{x-1}$

4) $\dfrac{1}{6b^2} + \dfrac{1}{6b} = \dfrac{1}{b^2}$

5) $\dfrac{2x-1}{5x+1} = \dfrac{3x-4}{x-7}$

6) $\dfrac{1}{3n^2} - \dfrac{1}{n} = \dfrac{1}{4n^2}$

7) $\dfrac{1}{8b^2} = \dfrac{1}{4b^2} - \dfrac{1}{2b}$

8) $\dfrac{1}{n-4} - 2 = \dfrac{3}{n-4}$

9) $\dfrac{4}{r-2} = -\dfrac{8}{r+2}$

10) $2 = \dfrac{2}{x^2+4x} + \dfrac{2x+2}{x}$

11) $\dfrac{3}{x} = 7 + \dfrac{2}{3x}$

12) $\dfrac{x+3}{x^2-x} - 2 = \dfrac{1}{x^2-x}$

13) $\dfrac{x-2}{x+5} - 1 = \dfrac{1}{x+2}$

14) $\dfrac{1}{12x^2} = \dfrac{1}{6x^2} - \dfrac{1}{2x}$

15) $\dfrac{x+3}{x^2+2x} = \dfrac{x}{x^2+2x} - \dfrac{6}{x+2}$

16) $1 = \dfrac{5}{2x^2+4x} + \dfrac{x+2}{2x}$

✍ **Simplify each expression.**

17) $\dfrac{\frac{3}{5}}{\frac{4}{45} - \frac{5}{18}} =$

18) $\dfrac{\frac{17}{2}}{-7\frac{4}{15}} =$

19) $\dfrac{7}{\frac{7}{x} + \frac{3}{4x}} =$

20) $\dfrac{2x^2}{\frac{3}{8} - \frac{3}{x}} =$

21) $\dfrac{\frac{2}{x-1} - \frac{1}{x+4}}{\frac{3}{x^2+9x+20}} =$

22) $\dfrac{\frac{14}{x-1}}{\frac{14}{7} - \frac{14}{42}} =$

23) $\dfrac{1 + \frac{8}{x-4}}{1 - \frac{4}{x-4}} =$

24) $\dfrac{\frac{1}{3} - \frac{x+2}{6}}{\frac{x^2}{4} - \frac{2}{3}} =$

Answers of Worksheets

Simplifying and Graphing rational expressions

1) $\frac{1}{3}$

2) $3(x + 2)$

3) $\frac{2}{x - 1}$

4) $\frac{x + 1}{x + 4}$

5) $\frac{2x^3}{3}$

6) $\frac{1}{x+5}$

7) $x + 2$

8) $\frac{6}{x - 1}$

9) Discontinuities: –2, 1;   Vertical Asymptote: $x = -2, x = 1$;   Holes: None

Horizontal. Asymptote: $y = -\frac{1}{4}$;   x–intercepts: None

10) Discontinuities –2, –3;   Vertical Asymptote $x = -3$;   Holes $x = -2$

Horizontal Asymptote $y = 0$; x–intercepts. None

11) Discontinuities: 7;   Vertical Asymptote: $x = 7$;   Holes: None

Horizontal Asymptote: $y = 1$;   x–intercepts: 2

12) Discontinuities: –1, 2;   Vertical Asymptote: $x = -1, x = 2$;   Holes: None

Horizontal Asymptote: $y = 1$;   x–intercepts: 0

13)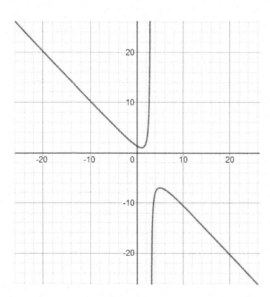

14)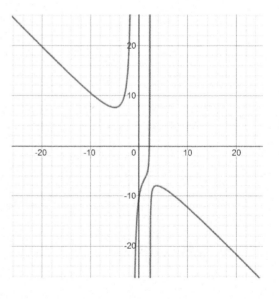

Adding and subtracting rational expressions

1) $\frac{x-2}{3x+7}$

2) $\frac{2x^2 + 3x + 14}{(x - 2)(x + 5)}$

3) $\frac{-3x-31}{(x + 3)(x - 8)}$

4) $\frac{2x - 7}{x^2 - 11}$

5) $\frac{2 + 2x}{x + 4}$

6) $\frac{x + 2}{x}$

7) $\frac{x-1}{x + 3}$

8) $\frac{27x^2 + 28x}{(3x + 5)(4x + 1)}$

9) $\frac{x^2 + y^2}{(x - y)(x + y)}$

10) $\dfrac{6}{(x+2)(x-4)(x-2)}$

11) $\dfrac{2x+2}{(x+4)(x+2)}$

12) $\dfrac{5x^2+18x-17}{3\,(x-1)(x+4)}$

13) $\dfrac{3x^2-2x-10}{(x+2)(x-2)}$

14) $\dfrac{9}{(x+2)(x+5)}$

15) $\dfrac{15x+47}{10x\,(x+3)}$

16) $\dfrac{x+2}{4}+3$

17) $\dfrac{12x^2+19x}{(3x+5)(3x+4)}$

18) $\dfrac{5}{4x(x+3)}$

Multiplying and Dividing rational expressions

1) $\dfrac{5}{6}$

2) $\dfrac{45}{4x}$

3) $\dfrac{150x}{29}$

4) $\dfrac{58x^2}{43}$

5) $\dfrac{32}{7x}$

6) $x+5$

7) 8

8) $\dfrac{2}{x+2}$

9) $\dfrac{9}{5x}$

10) $\dfrac{7x}{x-5}$

11) $\dfrac{5x}{x+6}$

12) $\dfrac{8}{7x}$

13) $\dfrac{x-3}{x-7}$

14) $-\dfrac{(x-6)}{72}$

15) $-\dfrac{x-1}{3x}$

16) 2

17) 8

18) $\dfrac{x+4}{x-10}$

19) $\dfrac{x+8}{44x}$

20) 12

21) $\dfrac{1}{5x}$

22) $\dfrac{x+2}{5x\,(x+6)}$

23) $\dfrac{x}{4}$

24) $\dfrac{7x^4}{x+9}$

25) $x+7$

26) $\dfrac{(x-2)(x+7)}{18}$

27) $\dfrac{x+6}{x+3}$

28) $\dfrac{x+9}{16x}$

Solving rational equations and complex fractions

1) $\{1, -9\}$

2) $\left\{\dfrac{1}{12}\right\}$

3) $\left\{\dfrac{-32}{3}, 0\right\}$

4) $\{5\}$

5) $\left\{-\dfrac{11}{13}, 1\right\}$

6) $\left\{\dfrac{1}{12}\right\}$

7) $\left\{\dfrac{1}{4}\right\}$

8) $\{3\}$

9) $\left\{\dfrac{2}{3}\right\}$

10) $\{-5\}$

11) $\left\{\dfrac{1}{3}\right\}$

12) $\left\{2, -\dfrac{1}{2}\right\}$

13) $\left\{-\dfrac{19}{8}\right\}$

14) $\left\{\dfrac{1}{6}\right\}$

15) $\left\{-\dfrac{1}{2}\right\}$

16) $\{3, -3\}$

17) $-\dfrac{54}{17}$

18) $-1\dfrac{37}{218}$

19) $\dfrac{28x}{31}$

20) $\dfrac{16x^3}{3x-24}$

21) $\dfrac{(x+9)(x+5)}{3\,(x-1)}$

22) $\dfrac{42}{5(x-1)}$

23) $\dfrac{x+4}{x-8}$

24) $-\dfrac{2x}{3x^2-8}$

Chapter 12 :

Statistics and Probability

Topics that you'll practice in this chapter:

- ✓ Mean and Median
- ✓ Mode and Range
- ✓ Probability Problems
- ✓ Factorials
- ✓ Combinations and Permutations

"The book of nature is written in the language of Mathematic" - Galileo.

Mean and Median

🖎 **Find Mean and Median of the Given Data.**

1) 8, 7, 14, 4, 8

2) 14, 8, 25, 19, 16, 33, 11

3) 23, 18, 15, 12, 17

4) 34, 14, 10, 15, 6, 11

5) 10, 19, 6, 8, 32, 20, 17

6) 17, 26, 39, 69, 20, 6

7) 40, 38, 18, 11, 9, 2, 7, 32, 41

8) 24, 21, 31, 12, 33, 32, 22

9) 16, 14, 20, 41, 15, 20, 38, 4

10) 20, 20, 30, 18, 6, 28, 12, 46

11) 12, 7, 10, 11, 16, 22

12) 10, 29, 27, 12, 2, 15, 10, 3

🖎 **Calculate.**

13) In a javelin throw competition, five athletics score 56, 34, 62, 23 and 19 meters. What are their Mean and Median? _____

14) Eva went to shop and bought 8 apples, 14 peaches, 6 bananas, 4 pineapples and 12 melons. What are the Mean and Median of her purchase? _____

15) Bob has 17 black pen, 19 red pen, 14 green pens, 20 blue pens and 5 boxes of yellow pens. If the Mean and Median are 19 respectively, what is the number of yellow pens in each box? _____

Mode and Range

✎ **Find Mode and Rage of the Given Data.**

1) 4, 3, 7, 3, 3, 4

    Mode: _____   Range: _____

2) 18, 18, 24, 26, 18, 8, 14, 22

    Mode: _____   Range: _____

3) 8, 8, 8, 16, 19, 22, 20, 9, 13

    Mode: _____   Range: _____

4) 24, 24, 14, 28, 20, 18, 20, 24

    Mode: _____   Range: _____

5) 6, 21, 27, 24, 27, 27

    Mode: _____   Range: _____

6) 21, 8, 8, 7, 8, 12, 10, 22, 18, 13

    Mode: _____   Range: _____

7) 7, 4, 4, 6, 13, 13, 13, 0, 2, 2

    Mode: _____   Range: _____

8) 5, 8, 5, 14, 12, 14, 3, 5, 18

    Mode: _____   Range: _____

9) 7, 7, 7, 12, 7, 3, 8, 16, 3, 17

    Mode: _____   Range: _____

10) 15, 15, 19, 16, 4, 16, 10, 15

    Mode: _____   Range: _____

11) 6, 6, 5, 6, 42, 13, 19, 2

    Mode: _____   Range: _____

12) 8, 8, 9, 8, 9, 4, 34, 22

    Mode: _____   Range: _____

✎ **Calculate.**

13) A stationery sold 12 pencils, 56 red pens, 24 blue pens, 20 notebooks, 12 erasers, 21 rulers and 11 color pencils. What are the Mode and Range for the stationery sells?

    Mode: _____   Range: _____

14) In an English test, eight students score 10, 15, 15, 18 18, 16, 15 and 15. What are their Mode and Range? _____

15) What is the range of the first 6 even numbers greater than 8?

    _____

Probability Problems

✎ **Calculate.**

1) A number is chosen at random from 1 to 10. Find the probability of selecting number 6 or smaller numbers. _____

2) Bag A contains 18 red marbles and 6 green marbles. Bag B contains 16 black marbles and 8 orange marbles. What is the probability of selecting a green marble at random from bag A? What is the probability of selecting a black marble at random from Bag B? _____

3) A number is chosen at random from 1 to 20. What is the probability of selecting multiples of 4? _____

4) A card is chosen from a well-shuffled deck of 52 cards. What is the probability that the card will be a queen? _____

5) A number is chosen at random from 1 to 15. What is the probability of selecting a multiple of 3 or 5? _____

A spinner numbered 1–8, is spun once. What is the probability of spinning …?

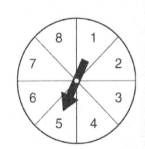

6) an Odd number? _____   7) a multiple of 2? _____

8) a multiple of 5? _____   9) number 10? _____

Factorials

✎ **Determine the value for each expression.**

1) $4! + 0! =$

2) $2! + 5! =$

3) $(2!)^2 =$

4) $5! - 3! =$

5) $6! - 3! + 10 =$

6) $3! \times 4 - 15 =$

7) $(2! + 3!)^2 =$

8) $(4! - 3!)^2 =$

9) $(3! \, 0!)^2 - 10 =$

10) $\dfrac{10!}{8!} =$

11) $\dfrac{6!}{4!} =$

12) $\dfrac{6!}{5!} =$

13) $\dfrac{15!}{13!} =$

14) $\dfrac{n!}{(n-3)!} =$

15) $\dfrac{(n+2)!}{n!} =$

16) $\dfrac{(2+2!)^3}{2!} =$

17) $\dfrac{5(n+2)!}{(n+1)!} =$

18) $\dfrac{22!}{20!4!} =$

19) $\dfrac{13!}{11!3!} =$

20) $\dfrac{9 \times 210!}{3(7 \times 30)!} =$

21) $\dfrac{32!}{31!2!} =$

22) $\dfrac{11!12!}{10!13!} =$

23) $\dfrac{16!15!}{14!14!} =$

24) $\dfrac{(5 \times 3)!}{0!14!} =$

25) $\dfrac{4!(5n-2)!}{(5n)!} =$

26) $\dfrac{4n(4n+7)!}{(4n+8)!} =$

27) $\dfrac{(n-2)!(n+1)}{(n+2)!} =$

Combinations and Permutations

✎ **Calculate the value of each.**

1) $6! =$ ____

2) $2! \times 5! =$ ____

3) $3 \times 4! =$ ____

4) $5! + 3! =$ ____

5) $7! =$ ____

6) $4! =$ ____

7) $3! + 3! =$ ____

8) $7! - 5! =$ ____

✎ **Find the answer for each word problems.**

9) Susan is baking cookies. She uses sugar, butter, Vanilla, eggs and flour. How many different orders of ingredients can she try? _____

10) Albert is planning for his vacation. He wants to go to museum, watch a movie, go to the beach, play the game and play football. How many ways of ordering are there for him? _____

11) How many 4-digit numbers can be named using the digits 3, 4, 5, and 6 without repetition? _____

12) In how many ways can 5 boys be arranged in a straight line? _____

13) In how many ways can 6 athletes be arranged in a straight line? _____

14) A professor is going to arrange her 7 students in a straight line. In how many ways can she do this? _____

15) How many code symbols can be formed with the letters for the word GAMES? _____

16) In how many ways a team of 7 basketball players can choose a captain and co-captain? _____

Answers of Worksheets

Mean and Median

1) Mean: 8.2, Median: 8
2) Mean: 18, Median: 16
3) Mean: 17, Median: 17
4) Mean: 15, Median: 12.5
5) Mean: 16, Median: 17
6) Mean: 29.5, Median: 23
7) Mean: 22, Median: 18
8) Mean: 25, Median: 24
9) Mean: 21, Median: 18
10) Mean: 22.5, Median: 20
11) Mean: 13, Median: 11.5
12) Mean: 13.5, Median: 11
13) Mean: 38.8, Median: 34
14) Mean: 8.8, Median: 8
15) 5

Mode and Range

1) Mode: 3, Range: 4
2) Mode: 18, Range: 18
3) Mode: 8, Range: 14
4) Mode: 24, Range: 14
5) Mode: 27, Range: 21
6) Mode: 8, Range: 15
7) Mode: 13, Range: 13
8) Mode: 5, Range: 15
9) Mode: 7, Range: 14
10) Mode: 15, Range: 15
11) Mode: 6, Range: 40
12) Mode: 8, Range: 30
13) Mode: 12, Range: 45
14) Mode: 15, Range: 8
15) 10

Probability Problems

1) $\frac{3}{5}$
2) $\frac{1}{4}, \frac{2}{3}$
3) $\frac{1}{4}$
4) $\frac{1}{13}$
5) $\frac{7}{15}$
6) $\frac{1}{2}$
7) $\frac{1}{2}$
8) $\frac{1}{8}$
9) 0

Factorials

1) 25
2) 122
3) 4
4) 114
5) 724
6) 9
7) 64
8) 324
9) 26
10) 90
11) 30
12) 6
13) 210
14) $n(n-1)(n-2)$
15) $(n+1)(n+2)$
16) 32
17) $5(n+2)$
18) 19.25
19) 26
20) 3
21) 16
22) $\frac{11}{13}$
23) 3,600
24) 15
25) $\frac{24}{5n(5n-1)}$
26) $\frac{n}{(n+2)}$
27) $\frac{1}{n(n-1)(n+2)}$

Combinations and Permutations

1) 720
2) 240
3) 72
4) 126
5) 5,040
6) 24

7) 12

8) 4,920

9) 120

10) 120

11) 24

12) 120

13) 720

14) 5,040

15) 120

16) 42

Chapter 13 :

Complex Numbers

Topics that you'll practice in this chapter:

✓ Adding and Subtracting Complex Numbers

✓ Multiplying and Dividing Complex Numbers

✓ Graphing Complex Numbers

✓ Rationalizing Imaginary Denominators

Mathematics is a hard thing to love. It has the unfortunate habit, like a rude dog, of turning its most unfavorable side towards you when you first make contact with it. — David Whiteland

Adding and Subtracting Complex Numbers

✎ **Simplify.**

1) $(7i) - (3i) =$

2) $(5i) + (4i) =$

3) $(2i) + (8i) =$

4) $(-8i) - (3i) =$

5) $(14i) + (6i) =$

6) $(6i) - (-10i) =$

7) $(-2i) + (-5i) =$

8) $(13i) - (5i) =$

9) $(-22i) - (11i) =$

10) $(-4i) + (2 + 6i) =$

11) $(10 - 5i) + (-3i) =$

12) $(-8i) + (6 + 12i) =$

13) $1 + (5 - 4i) =$

14) $(13i) - (-8 + 2i) =$

15) $(8 + 12i) - (-10i) =$

16) $(10 + i) + (-5i) =$

17) $(11i) - (-7i + 9) =$

18) $(10i + 12) + (-2i) =$

19) $(20) - (16 + 4i) =$

20) $(3 + 3i) + (8 + 4i) =$

21) $(15 - 7i) + (3 + 4i) =$

22) $(12 + 6i) + (10 + 17i) =$

23) $(-5 + 6i) - (-16 - 12i) =$

24) $(-4 + 14i) - (-9 + 11i) =$

25) $(-22 + 4i) - (-7 - 22i) =$

26) $(-26 - 18i) + (3 + 34i) =$

27) $(-19 - 13i) - (-7 - 20i) =$

28) $-21 + (5i) + (-32 + 14i) =$

29) $30 - (7i) + (3 - 11i) =$

30) $28 + (-32 - 10i) - 7 =$

31) $(-44i) + (2 - 7i) + 9 =$

32) $(-21i) - (12 - 9i) + 21i =$

Multiplying and Dividing Complex Numbers

✎ **Simplify.**

1) $(5i)(-3i) =$

2) $(-8i)(2i) =$

3) $(3i)(-3i)(-3i) =$

4) $(6i)(-6i) =$

5) $(-3 - 4i)(2 + i) =$

6) $(5 - 2i)^2 =$

7) $(5 - 2i)(6 - 4i) =$

8) $(1 + 6i)^2 =$

9) $(5i)(-3i)(2 - 4i) =$

10) $(11 - 2i)(2 - 4i) =$

11) $(-3 + i)(6 + 5i) =$

12) $(2 - 8i)(6 - 4i) =$

13) $3(4i) - (6i)(-2 + 5i) =$

14) $\dfrac{5}{-25i} =$

15) $\dfrac{3-4i}{-5i} =$

16) $\dfrac{6+12i}{2i} =$

17) $\dfrac{20i}{-5+4i} =$

18) $\dfrac{-6-9i}{4i} =$

19) $\dfrac{4i}{8-2i} =$

20) $\dfrac{4-7i}{6-2i} =$

21) $\dfrac{3-2i}{-1-1i} =$

22) $\dfrac{-5-5i}{-4-i} =$

23) $\dfrac{-6+2i}{-10-4i} =$

24) $\dfrac{-8-4i}{-2+4i} =$

25) $\dfrac{2+3i}{1-4i} =$

Graphing Complex Numbers

✍ **Identify each complex number graphed.**

1)

2)

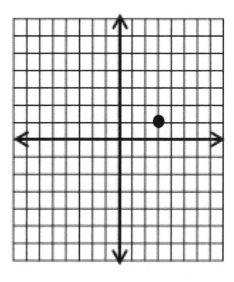

3)

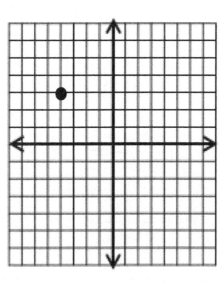

4)

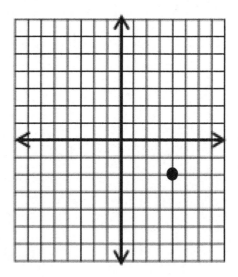

Rationalizing Imaginary Denominators

✎ **Simplify.**

1) $\dfrac{-7}{-7i} =$

2) $\dfrac{-3}{-15i} =$

3) $\dfrac{-3}{-39i} =$

4) $\dfrac{24}{-3i} =$

5) $\dfrac{5}{2i} =$

6) $\dfrac{16}{-4i} =$

7) $\dfrac{14}{-6i} =$

8) $\dfrac{-17}{3i} =$

9) $\dfrac{4x}{5yi} =$

10) $\dfrac{10-10i}{-2i} =$

11) $\dfrac{5-11i}{-i} =$

12) $\dfrac{21+4i}{4i} =$

13) $\dfrac{8i}{-1+4i} =$

14) $\dfrac{10i}{-6+8i} =$

15) $\dfrac{-25-5i}{-5+5i} =$

16) $\dfrac{-7-2i}{3+1i} =$

17) $\dfrac{-12-6i}{8-6i} =$

18) $\dfrac{-14+7i}{-7i} =$

19) $\dfrac{12+3i}{3i} =$

20) $\dfrac{-2-i}{4-3i} =$

21) $\dfrac{-11+4i}{-5i} =$

22) $\dfrac{8+2i}{-5-2i} =$

23) $\dfrac{-9-5i}{-8-2i} =$

24) $\dfrac{4i-1}{-5-2i} =$

Answers of Worksheets

Adding and Subtracting Complex Numbers

1) $4i$	9) $-33i$	17) $-9 + 18i$	25) $-15 + 26i$
2) $9i$	10) $2 + 2i$	18) $12 + 8i$	26) $-23 + 16i$
3) $10i$	11) $10 - 8i$	19) $4 - 4i$	27) $-12 + 7i$
4) $-11i$	12) $6 + 4i$	20) $11 + 7i$	28) $-53 + 19i$
5) $20i$	13) $6 - 4i$	21) $18 - 3i$	29) $33 - 18i$
6) $16i$	14) $8 + 11i$	22) $22 + 23i$	30) $-11 - 10i$
7) $-7i$	15) $8 + 22i$	23) $11 + 18i$	31) $11 - 51i$
8) $8i$	16) $10 - 4i$	24) $5 + 3i$	32) $-12 + 9i$

Multiplying and Dividing Complex Numbers

1) 15	9) $30 - 60i$	16) $-6 + 3i$	22) $\frac{25}{17} + \frac{15}{17}i$
2) 16	10) $14 - 48i$	17) $\frac{80}{41} - \frac{100}{41}i$	23) $\frac{13}{29} - \frac{11}{29}i$
3) $-27i$	11) $-23 - 9i$	18) $\frac{9}{4} - \frac{3}{2}i$	24) $2i$
4) 36	12) $-20 - 56i$		
5) $-2 - 11i$	13) $30 + 24i$	19) $-\frac{2}{17} + \frac{8}{17}i$	25) $-\frac{10}{17} + \frac{11}{17}i$
6) $21 - 20i$	14) $\frac{i}{5}$	20) $\frac{19}{20} - \frac{17}{20}i$	
7) $22 - 32i$	15) $\frac{4}{5} + \frac{3}{5}i$	21) $-\frac{1}{2} + \frac{5}{2}i$	
8) $-35 + 12i$			

Graphing Complex Numbers

1) $-4 - 3i$	2) $3 + i$	3) $-4 + 3i$	4) $4 - 2i$

Rationalizing Imaginary Denominators

1) $-i$	7) $\frac{7}{3}i$	13) $\frac{32}{17} - \frac{8}{17}i$	19) $1 - 4i$
2) $-\frac{1}{5}i$	8) $\frac{17}{3}i$	14) $\frac{4}{5} - \frac{3}{5}i$	20) $-\frac{1}{5} - \frac{2}{5}i$
3) $\frac{-1}{13}i$	9) $-\frac{4x}{5y}i$	15) $2 + 3i$	21) $-\frac{4}{5} - \frac{11}{5}i$
4) $8i$	10) $5 + 5i$	16) $-\frac{23}{10} + \frac{1}{10}i$	22) $-\frac{44}{29} + \frac{6}{29}i$
5) $-\frac{5}{2}i$	11) $11 + 5i$	17) $-\frac{3}{5} - \frac{6}{5}i$	23) $\frac{41}{34} + \frac{11}{34}i$
6) $4i$	12) $1 - \frac{21}{4}i$	18) $-1 - 2i$	24) $-\frac{3}{29} - \frac{22}{29}i$

Chapter 14 :

Logarithms

Topics that you'll practice in this chapter:

- ✓ Rewriting Logarithms
- ✓ Evaluating Logarithms
- ✓ Properties of Logarithms
- ✓ Natural Logarithms
- ✓ Exponential Equations Requiring Logarithms
- ✓ Solving Logarithmic Equations

Mathematics is an art of human understanding. — William Thurston

Rewriting Logarithms

✍ **Rewrite each equation in exponential form.**

1) $\log_3 27 = 3$

2) $\log_2 128 = 7$

3) $\log_6 1{,}296 = 4$

4) $\log_5 625 = 4$

5) $\log_{11} 121 = 2$

6) $\log_{12} 1{,}728 = 3$

7) $\log_9 729 = 3$

8) $\log_3 729 = 6$

9) $\log_{10} 10{,}000 = 4$

10) $\log_7 343 = 3$

11) $\log_4 1{,}024 = 5$

12) $\log_{12} 144 = 2$

13) $\log_{13} 2{,}197 = 3$

14) $\log_{25} 5 = \frac{1}{2}$

15) $\log_{81} 3 = \frac{1}{4}$

16) $\log_{3{,}125} 5 = \frac{1}{5}$

17) $\log_{1{,}000} 10 = \frac{1}{3}$

18) $\log_5 \frac{1}{125} = -3$

19) $\log_4 \frac{1}{16} = -2$

20) $\log_a \frac{7}{4} = b$

✍ **Rewrite each exponential equation in logarithmic form.**

21) $2^5 = 32$

22) $4^3 = 64$

23) $5^4 = 625$

24) $11^3 = 1{,}331$

25) $3^5 = 243$

26) $6^4 = 1{,}296$

27) $7^4 = 2{,}401$

28) $9^3 = 729$

29) $4^{-5} = \frac{1}{1{,}024}$

30) $3^{-8} = \frac{1}{6{,}561}$

31) $11^{-2} = \frac{1}{121}$

32) $12^{-3} = \frac{1}{1{,}728}$

33) $4^{-5} = \frac{1}{1{,}024}$

34) $10^{-5} = \frac{1}{100{,}000}$

Evaluating Logarithms

✍ **Evaluate each logarithm.**

1) $\log_3 729 =$

2) $\log_2 256 =$

3) $\log_3 243 =$

4) $\log_4 64 =$

5) $\log_8 64 =$

6) $\log_{11} 121 =$

7) $\log_{10} 10,000 =$

8) $\log_5 \frac{1}{25} =$

9) $\log_4 \frac{1}{256} =$

10) $\log_2 \frac{1}{32} =$

11) $\log_6 \frac{1}{36} =$

12) $\log_9 \frac{1}{81} =$

13) $\log_{12} \frac{1}{144} =$

14) $\log_{1,000} \frac{1}{10} =$

15) $\log_{243} 3 =$

16) $\log_4 \frac{1}{16} =$

17) $\log_8 \frac{1}{512} =$

18) $\log_3 \frac{1}{81} =$

✍ **Circle the points which are on the graph of the given logarithmic functions.**

19) $y = 4\log_4(3x - 2) + 1$ $(3,4),$ $(2,5),$ $(7,4)$

20) $y = 5\log_6(12x) - 7$ $(2,-2),$ $(\frac{1}{3}, 12),$ $(\frac{1}{2}, -2)$

21) $y = -2\log_3 9(x - 5) + 5$ $(6,-3),$ $(8,-1),$ $(1,6)$

22) $y = \frac{1}{4}\log_6(6x) + \frac{1}{2}$ $(6,1),$ $(6,\frac{1}{4}),$ $(4,\frac{1}{4})$

23) $y = -2\log_8 8(x + 4) + 9$ $(-4,0),$ $(0,9),$ $(-2,6\frac{1}{3})$

24) $y = -\log_5(x + 15) - 6$ $(10,-\frac{1}{5}),$ $(10,-8),$ $(11,-\frac{2}{5})$

25) $y = -3\log_2(2x + 6) + 7$ $(5,-5),$ $(-5,-5),$ $(-2,-2)$

Properties of Logarithms

✎ **Expand each logarithm.**

1) $\log(11 \times 4) =$

2) $\log(13 \times 5) =$

3) $\log(4 \times 12) =$

4) $\log\left(\frac{2}{7}\right) =$

5) $\log\left(\frac{4}{9}\right) =$

6) $\log\left(\frac{5}{8}\right)^3 =$

7) $\log(6 \times 5^4) =$

8) $\log\left(\frac{14}{3}\right)^5 =$

9) $\log\left(\frac{3^4}{8}\right) =$

10) $\log(x \times y)^8 =$

11) $\log(x^6 \times y^{12} \times z^2) =$

12) $\log\left(\frac{u^8}{v^3}\right) =$

13) $\log\left(\frac{x}{y^7}\right) =$

✎ **Condense each expression to a single logarithm.**

14) $\log 8 - \log 13 =$

15) $\log 6 + \log 11 =$

16) $4\log 2 - 7\log 5 =$

17) $10\log 4 - 3\log 7 =$

18) $3\log 9 - \log 17 =$

19) $11\log 6 - 9\log 4 =$

20) $\log 15 - 6\log 7 =$

21) $6\log 8 + 4\log 10 =$

22) $12\log 5 + 14\log 9 =$

23) $17\log_8 a + 6\log_8 b =$

24) $2\log_9 x - 3\log_9 y =$

25) $\log_{11} u - 16\log_{11} v =$

26) $8\log_{15} u + 9\log_{15} v =$

27) $32\log_6 u - 25\log_6 v =$

Natural Logarithms

✎ **Solve each equation for** x.

1) $e^x = 9$

2) $e^x = 36$

3) $e^x = 49$

4) $\ln x = 3$

5) $\ln(\ln x) = 7$

6) $e^x = 4$

7) $\ln(5x + 2) = 1$

8) $\ln(7x + 4) = 3$

9) $\ln(9x + 5) = 4$

10) $\ln x = \frac{1}{9}$

11) $\ln 11x = e^5$

12) $\ln x = \ln 6 + \ln 7$

13) $\ln x = 4\ln 3 + \ln 2$

✎ **Evaluate without using a calculator.**

14) $11\ln e =$

15) $\ln e^{10} =$

16) $4 \ln e =$

17) $\ln e^{21} =$

18) $32\ln e =$

19) $4\ln e^5 =$

20) $e^{\ln 22} =$

21) $e^{3\ln 3} =$

22) $e^{3\ln 5} =$

23) $\ln \sqrt[11]{e} =$

✎ **Reduce the following expressions to simplest form.**

24) $e^{-4ln9+4ln3} =$

25) $e^{-3ln\left(\frac{5}{4e}\right)} =$

26) $2\,ln(e^4) =$

27) $ln\left(\frac{1}{e}\right)^4 =$

28) $e^{ln9+3ln3} =$

29) $e^{ln\left(\frac{13}{e}\right)} =$

30) $8\,ln(1^{-3e}) =$

31) $2\,ln\left(\frac{1}{e}\right)^{-3} =$

32) $6ln\left(\frac{\sqrt[3]{e}}{3e}\right) =$

33) $e^{-4lne+2ln5} =$

34) $e^{ln\frac{4}{e}} =$

35) $11\,ln(e^e) =$

Exponential Equations and Logarithms

✍ **Solve each equation for the unknown variable.**

1) $3^{4n} = 243$

2) $5^{3r} = 625$

3) $6^{2n-1} = 216$

4) $16^{2r+3} = 4$

5) $169^{2x} = 13$

6) $7^{-3v-3} = 49$

7) $2^{4n} = 128$

8) $11^{n-1} = 1,331$

9) $\frac{9^{3a}}{3^{2a}} = 729$

10) $13^5 \times 13^{-4v} = 169$

11) $4^{3n} = \frac{1}{64}$

12) $(\frac{1}{11})^{2n} = 121$

13) $2,187^{3x} = 3$

14) $13^{5-7x} = 13^{-2x}$

15) $11^{-3x} = 11^{2x-7}$

16) $3^{5n} = 243$

17) $17^{5x+3} = 17^{6x}$

18) $15^{3n} = 225$

19) $4^{-3k} = 512$

20) $8^{-4r} = 8^{-5r+2}$

21) $8^{2x+3} = 8^{5x}$

22) $10^{3x-2} = 100,000$

23) $16 \times 64^{-v} = 128$

24) $\frac{128}{2^{-3m}} = 2^{4m+5}$

25) $14^{-5n} \times 14^{2n+3} = 14^{-2n}$

26) $(\frac{1}{9})^{4n+3} \times (\frac{1}{9})^{-3n-8} = (\frac{1}{9})^{-4n}$

✍ **Solve each problem. (Round to the nearest whole number)**

27) A substance decays 16% each day. After 8 days, there are 6 milligrams of the substance remaining. How many milligrams were there initially? _____

28) A culture of bacteria grows continuously. The culture doubles every 4 hours. If the initial number of bacteria is 20, how many bacteria will there be in 13 hours?

_____

29) Bob plans to invest $11,200 at an annual rate of 3.5%. How much will Bob have in the account after three years if the balance is compounded quarterly? _____

30) Suppose you plan to invest $8,000 at an annual rate of 5%. How much will you have in the account after 6 years if the balance is compounded monthly? _____

Solving Logarithmic Equations

✍ **Find the value of the variables in each equation.**

1) $2\log(x) + 5 = 9$

2) $\log_4 4x + 3 = 5$

3) $-\log_8(8x) + 2 = 3$

4) $\log 2x - \log 4 = 1$

5) $\log 5x + \log 25 = 1$

6) $\log 4 - \log x = 3$

7) $\log 4x + \log 2 = \log 16$

8) $-6\log_3(5x - 1) = -36$

9) $\log 4x = \log(8x - 1)$

10) $\log(4k - 6) = \log(k - 3)$

11) $\log(5p + 2) = \log(p + 4)$

12) $-30 + \log_4(3n + 2) = -30$

13) $\log_4(4x - 4) = \log_4(x^2)$

14) $\log_8(k^2 + 15) = \log_8(-6k - 3)$

15) $\log(16 + 6b) = \log(10b^2 + 12b)$

16) $\log_6(2x + 5) - \log_6 x = \log_6 9$

17) $\log_5 5 + \log_5(x^2 + 1) = \log_5 25$

18) $\log_6(x + 3) + \log_6(x + 1) =$

$\log_6 8$

✍ **Find the value of x in each natural logarithm equation.**

19) $\ln 8 - \ln(4x + 8) = 4$

20) $\ln(x + 5) - \ln(x + 2) = \ln 10$

21) $\ln e^6 - \ln(x - 1) = 3$

22) $\ln(2x - 8) + \ln(x - 4) = \ln 8$

23) $\ln 5x - \ln(x + 4) = \ln 2$

24) $\ln(8x - 4) - \ln(x - 2) = \ln 25$

25) $\ln(3x + 2) - 4\ln 2 = 5$

26) $\ln(2x - 5) + \ln(x - 3) = \ln 6$

27) $\ln(x - 1) + \ln(4x - 7) = \ln(7)$

28) $2\ln 3x - \ln(x + 10) = \ln 2x$

29) $\ln x^4 + \ln x^8 = 4\ln(2x)$

30) $\ln x^{10} - \ln(x^2 + 10) = 10\ln 2x$

31) $8\ln(x - 2) = 4\ln(x^2 - 4x + 4)$

32) $\ln(x^4 + 10) = \ln(x^2 + 9)$

33) $2\ln x - 2\ln(x + 8) = \ln(x^2)$

34) $\ln(2x + 1) - \ln(4x + 1) = \ln 4$

35) $\ln 16 + 2\ln(x - 2) = \ln 4$

36) $\ln e^2 + \ln(5x - 6) = \ln(5) + 3$

ALEKS Subject Test Mathematics

Answers of Worksheets

Rewriting Logarithms

1) $3^3 = 27$

2) $2^7 = 128$

3) $6^4 = 1,296$

4) $5^4 = 625$

5) $11^2 = 121$

6) $12^3 = 1,728$

7) $9^3 = 729$

8) $3^6 = 729$

9) $10^4 = 10,000$

10) $7^3 = 343$

11) $4^5 = 1,024$

12) $12^2 = 144$

13) $13^3 = 2,197$

14) $25^{\frac{1}{2}} = 5$

15) $81^{\frac{1}{4}} = 3$

16) $3,125^{\frac{1}{5}} = 5$

17) $1,000^{\frac{1}{3}} = 10$

18) $5^{-3} = \frac{1}{125}$

19) $4^{-2} = \frac{1}{16}$

20) $a^b = \frac{7}{4}$

21) $\log_2 32 = 5$

22) $\log_4 64 = 3$

23) $\log_5 625 = 4$

24) $\log_{11} 1,331 = 3$

25) $\log_3 243 = 5$

26) $\log_6 1,296 = 4$

27) $\log_7 2,401 = 4$

28) $\log_9 729 = 3$

29) $\log_4 \frac{1}{1,024} = -5$

30) $\log_3 \frac{1}{6,561} = -8$

31) $\log_{11} \frac{1}{121} = -2$

32) $\log_{12} \frac{1}{1,728} = -3$

33) $\log_4 \frac{1}{1,024} = -5$

34) $\log_{10} \frac{1}{100,000} = -5$

Evaluating Logarithms

1) 6

2) 8

3) 5

4) 3

5) 2

6) 2

7) 4

8) -2

9) -4

10) -5

11) -2

12) -2

13) -2

14) $-\frac{1}{3}$

15) $\frac{1}{5}$

16) -2

17) -3

18) -4

19) $(2,5)$

20) $(\frac{1}{2}, -2)$

21) $(8, -1)$

22) $(6, 1)$

23) $(-2, 6\frac{1}{3})$

24) $(10, -8)$

25) $(5, -5)$

Properties of Logarithms

1) $\log 11 + \log 4$

2) $\log 13 + \log 5$

3) $\log 4 + \log 12$

4) $\log 2 - \log 7$

5) $\log 4 - \log 9$

6) $3 \log 5 - 3 \log 8$

7) $\log 6 + 4 \log 5$

8) $5\log 14 - 5 \log 3$

9) $4 \log 3 - \log 8$

10) $8 \log x + 8 \log y$

11) $6\log x + 12\log y + 2\log z$

12) $8\log u - 3\log v$

13) $\log x - 7\log y$

14) $\log \frac{8}{13}$

15) $\log(6 \times 11)$

16) $\log \frac{2^4}{5^7}$

17) $\log \frac{4^{10}}{7^3}$

18) $\log \frac{9^3}{17}$

19) $\log \frac{6^{11}}{4^9}$

20) $\log \frac{15}{7^6}$

21) $\log(8^6 \times 10^4)$

22) $\log(5^{12} \times 9^{14})$

23) $\log_8 (a^{17}b^6)$

24) $\log_9 \frac{x^2}{y^3}$

25) $\log_{11} \frac{u}{v^{16}}$

26) $\log_{15}(u^8 \times v^9)$

27) $\log_6 \frac{u^{32}}{v^{25}}$

Natural Logarithms

1) $x = \ln 9$

2) $x = \ln 36, x = 2\ln(6)$

3) $x = \ln 49, x = 2\ln(7)$

4) $x = e^3$

5) $x = e^{e^7}$

6) $x = \ln 4$

7) $x = \frac{e-2}{5}$

8) $x = \frac{e^3-4}{7}$

9) $x = \frac{e^4-5}{9}$

10) $x = \sqrt[9]{e}$

11) $x = \frac{e \, e^5}{11}$

12) $x = 42$

13) $x = 162$

14) 11

15) 10

16) 4

17) 21

18) 32

19) 20

20) 22

21) 27

22) 125

23) $\frac{1}{11}$

24) $\frac{1}{81}$

25) $\frac{64e^3}{125}$

26) 8

27) -4

28) 243

29) $\frac{13}{e}$

30) 0

31) 6

32) $\ln\left(\frac{1}{3^6 e^4}\right) = -10.6$

33) $25e^{-4} = \frac{25}{e^4}$

34) $\frac{4}{e}$

35) $11e$

Exponential Equations and Logarithms

1) $\frac{5}{4}$

2) $\frac{4}{3}$

3) 2

4) $-\frac{5}{4}$

5) $\frac{1}{4}$

6) $-\frac{5}{3}$

7) $\frac{7}{4}$

8) 4

9) $\frac{3}{2}$

10) $\frac{3}{4}$

11) -1

12) -1

13) $\frac{1}{21}$

14) 1

15) $\frac{7}{5}$

16) 1

17) 3

18) $\frac{2}{3}$

19) $-\frac{3}{2}$

20) 2

21) 1

22) $\frac{7}{3}$

23) $-\frac{1}{2}$

24) 2

25) 3

26) 1

27) 24.2

28) 190.27

29) $\$12,432.4$

30) $\$10,792.14$

Solving Logarithmic Equations

1) $\{100\}$

2) $\{4\}$

3) $\{\frac{1}{64}\}$

4) $\{20\}$

5) $\{\frac{2}{25}\}$

6) $\{\frac{1}{250}\}$

7) $\{2\}$

8) $\{146\}$

9) $\{\frac{1}{4}\}$

10) No Solution

11) $\{\frac{1}{2}\}$

12) $\{-\frac{1}{3}\}$

13) $\{2\}$

14) No Solution

15) $\{1, -\frac{8}{5}\}$

16) $\{\frac{5}{7}\}$

17) $\{2, -2\}$

18) $\{1\}$

19) $x = \frac{8 - 8e^4}{4e^4}$

20) $\{-\frac{5}{3}\}$

21) $e^3 + 1$

22) $\{6\}$

23) $\{\frac{8}{3}\}$

24) $\{\frac{46}{17}\}$

25) $x = \frac{16e^5 - 2}{3}$

26) $x = \frac{9}{2}$

27) $x = \frac{11}{4}$

28) $x = \frac{20}{7}$

29) $e^{\frac{\ln(2)}{2}}$

30) No Solution

31) $x > 2$

32) No Solution

33) No Solution

34) $x = -\frac{3}{14}$

35) $x = \frac{5}{2}$

36) $x = \frac{5e + 6}{5}$

Chapter 15 :

Geometry and Solid Figures

Topics that you will practice in this chapter:

- ✓ Angles
- ✓ Pythagorean Relationship
- ✓ Triangles
- ✓ Polygons
- ✓ Trapezoids
- ✓ Circles
- ✓ Cubes
- ✓ Rectangular Prism
- ✓ Cylinder
- ✓ Pyramids and Cone

Geometry is the archetype of the beauty of the world.

Johannes Kepler

Angles

✍ **What is the value of x in the following figures?**

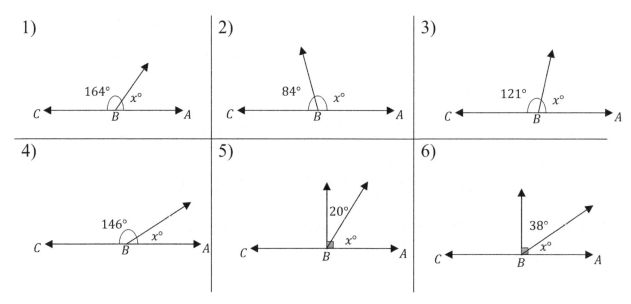

✍ **Calculate.**

7) Two supplement angles have equal measures. What is the measure of each angle? _____

8) The measure of an angle is seven fifth the measure of its supplement. What is the measure of the angle? _____

9) Two angles are complementary and the measure of one angle is 24 less than the other. What is the measure of the smaller angle? _____

10) Two angles are complementary. The measure of one angle is one fifth the measure of the other. What is the measure of the bigger angle? _____

11) Two supplementary angles are given. The measure of one angle is 40° less than the measure of the other. What does the smaller angle measure? _____

Pythagorean Theorem

✍ **Do the following lengths form a right triangle?**

1)
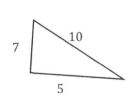

2)
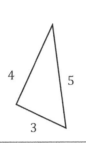

3)
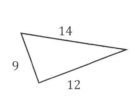

4)
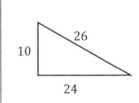

5)
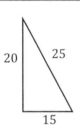

6)
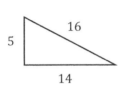

7)
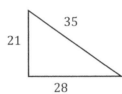

8)
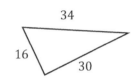

✍ **Find the missing side?**

9)
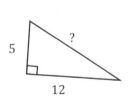

10)
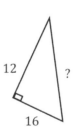

11)
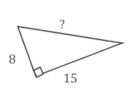

12)
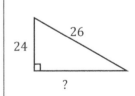

13)
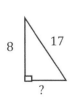

14)
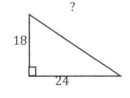

15)
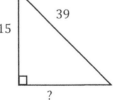

16)

Triangles

✎ **Find the measure of the unknown angle in each triangle.**

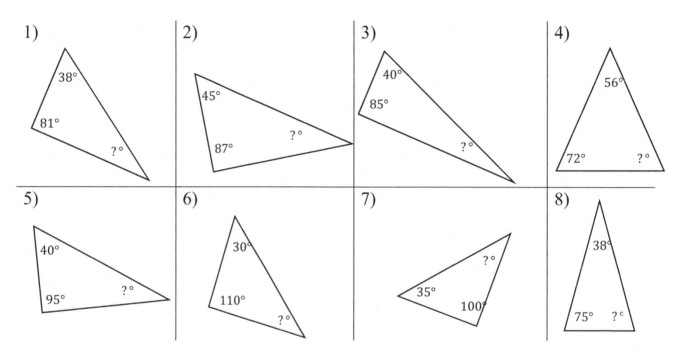

1)

38°
81°
?°

2)

45°
87°
?°

3)

40°
85°
?°

4)

56°
72°   ?°

5)

40°
95°   ?°

6)

30°
110°
?°

7)

?°
35°
100°

8)

38°
75°   ?°

✎ **Find area of each triangle.**

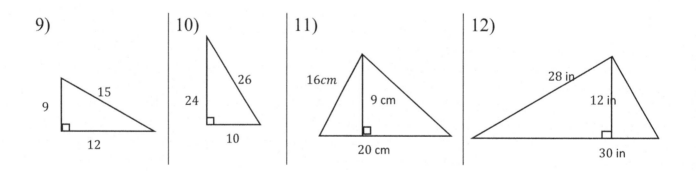

9)

9
15
12

10)

26
24
10

11)

16cm
9 cm
20 cm

12)

28 in
12 in
30 in

Polygons

✍ **Find the perimeter of each shape.**

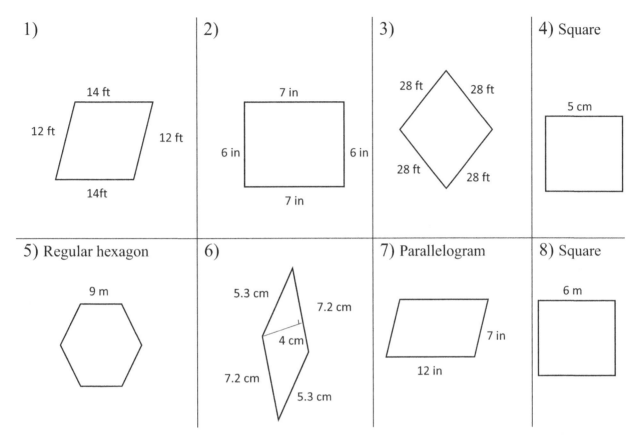

1)

14 ft

12 ft   12 ft

14ft

2)

7 in

6 in   6 in

7 in

3)

28 ft   28 ft

28 ft   28 ft

4) Square

5 cm

5) Regular hexagon

9 m

6)

5.3 cm

7.2 cm

4 cm

7.2 cm

5.3 cm

7) Parallelogram

7 in

12 in

8) Square

6 m

✍ **Find the area of each shape.**

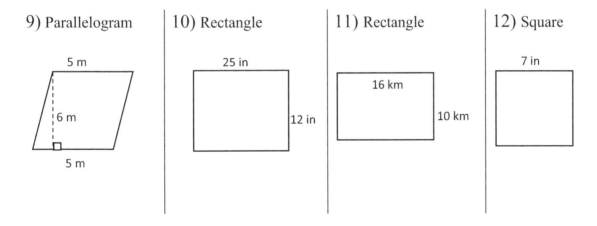

9) Parallelogram

5 m

6 m

5 m

10) Rectangle

25 in

12 in

11) Rectangle

16 km

10 km

12) Square

7 in

Trapezoids

✏️ **Find the area of each trapezoid.**

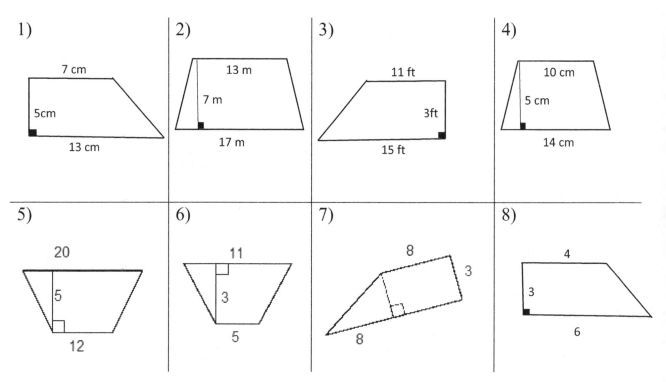

1)

7 cm

5cm

13 cm

2)

13 m

7 m

17 m

3)

11 ft

3ft

15 ft

4)

10 cm

5 cm

14 cm

5)

20

5

12

6)

11

3

5

7)

8

3

8

8)

4

3

6

✏️ **Calculate.**

1) A trapezoid has an area of 45 cm² and its height is 5 cm and one base is 5 cm. What is the other base length? _____

2) If a trapezoid has an area of 99 ft² and the lengths of the bases are 8 ft and 10 ft, find the height? _____

3) If a trapezoid has an area of 126 m² and its height is 14 m and one base is 6 m, find the other base length? _____

4) The area of a trapezoid is 440 ft² and its height is 22 ft. If one base of the trapezoid is 15 ft, what is the other base length?

_____

Circles

✍ **Find the area of each circle.** ($\pi = 3.14$)

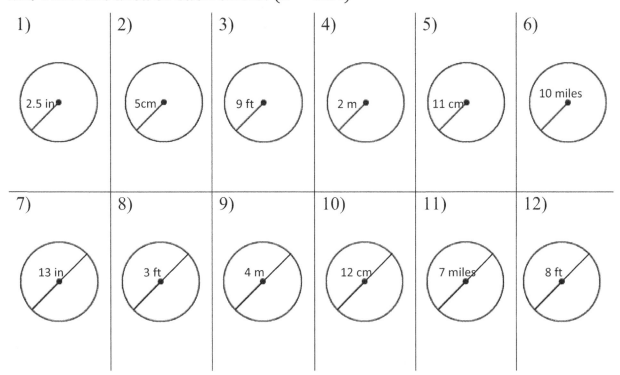

| 1) 2.5 in | 2) 5cm | 3) 9 ft | 4) 2 m | 5) 11 cm | 6) 10 miles |
| 7) 13 in | 8) 3 ft | 9) 4 m | 10) 12 cm | 11) 7 miles | 12) 8 ft |

✍ **Complete the table below.** ($\pi = 3.14$)

Circle No.	Radius	Diameter	Circumference	Area
1	1 *in*	2 *in*	6.28 *in*	3.14 in^2
2		10 *m*		
3				28.26 ft^2
4			47.1 *mi*	
5		11 *km*		
6	7 *cm*			
7		12 *ft*		
8				314 m^2
9			56.52 *in*	
10	4.5 *ft*			

Cubes

✎ **Find the volume of each cube.**

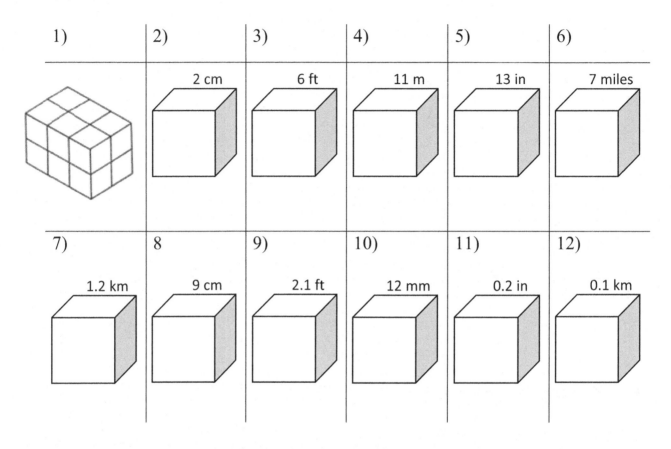

1)

2) 2 cm

3) 6 ft

4) 11 m

5) 13 in

6) 7 miles

7) 1.2 km

8) 9 cm

9) 2.1 ft

10) 12 mm

11) 0.2 in

12) 0.1 km

✎ **Find the surface area of each cube.**

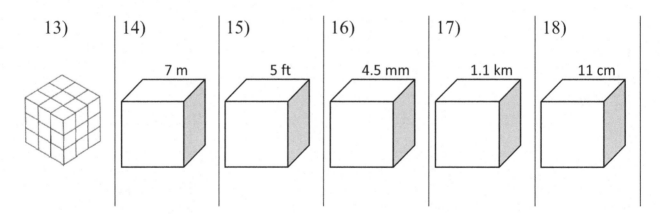

13)

14) 7 m

15) 5 ft

16) 4.5 mm

17) 1.1 km

18) 11 cm

Rectangular Prism

✎ **Find the volume of each Rectangular Prism.**

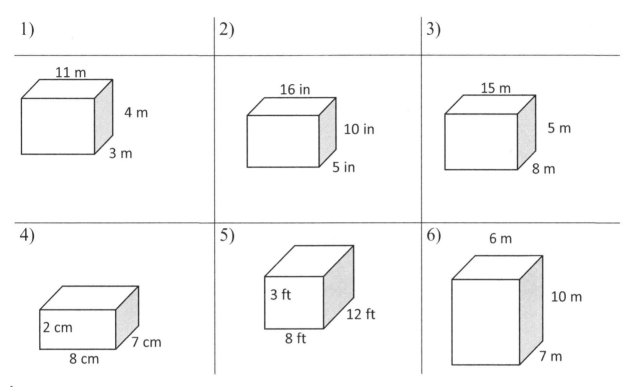

1)

11 m
4 m
3 m

2)

16 in
10 in
5 in

3)

15 m
5 m
8 m

4)

2 cm
7 cm
8 cm

5)

3 ft
12 ft
8 ft

6)

6 m
10 m
7 m

✎ **Find the surface area of each Rectangular Prism.**

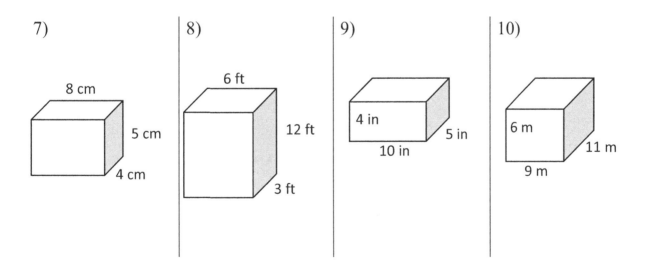

7)

8 cm
5 cm
4 cm

8)

6 ft
12 ft
3 ft

9)

4 in
10 in
5 in

10)

6 m
11 m
9 m

Cylinder

✏ **Find the volume of each Cylinder. Round your answer to the nearest tenth.** ($\pi = 3.14$)

1)
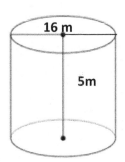
16 m

5m

2)

15.5 cm

4.2 cm

3)
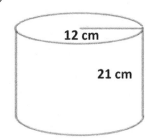
12 cm

21 cm

4)
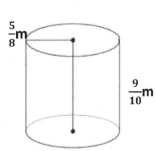
$\frac{5}{8}$m

$\frac{9}{10}$m

5)
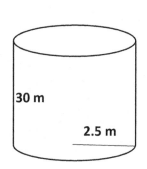
30 m

2.5 m

6)
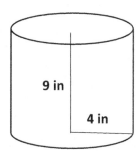
9 in

4 in

✏ **Find the surface area of each Cylinder.** ($\pi = 3.14$)

7)
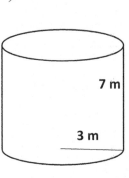
7 m

3 m

8)
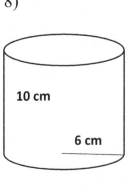
10 cm

6 cm

9)
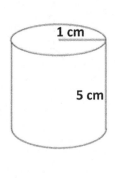
1 cm

5 cm

10)
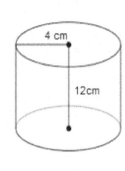
4 cm

12cm

Pyramids and Cone

✒ **Find the volume of each Pyramid and Cone.** ($\pi = 3.14$)

1)

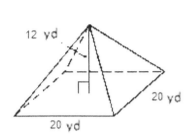

12 yd
20 yd
20 yd

2)

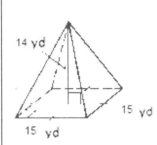

14 yd
15 yd
15 yd

3)

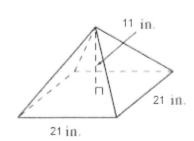

11 in.
21 in.
21 in.

4)

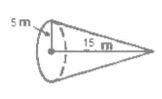

5 m
15 m

5)

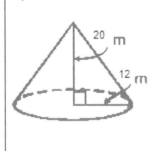

20 m
12 m

6)

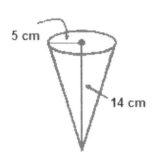

5 cm
14 cm

✒ **Find the surface area of each Pyramid and Cone.** ($\pi = 3.14$)

7)

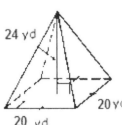

24 yd
20 yd
20 yd

8)

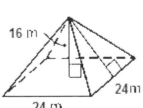

16 m
24 m
24 m

9)

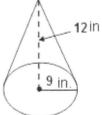

12 in
9 in.

10)

16 cm
12 cm

Answers of Worksheets

Angles

1) 16°	4) 34°	7) 90°	10) 75°
2) 96°	5) 70°	8) 75°	11) 70°
3) 59°	6) 52°	9) 33°	

Pythagorean Relationship

1) No	5) Yes	9) 13	13) 15
2) Yes	6) No	10) 20	14) 30
3) No	7) Yes	11) 17	15) 36
4) Yes	8) Yes	12) 10	16) 12

Triangles

1) 60°	5) 45°	9) 54 $square$ $unites$
2) 48°	6) 40°	10) 120 $square$ $unites$
3) 55°	7) 45°	11) 90 $square$ $unites$
4) 52°	8) 67°	12) 180 $square$ $unites$

Polygons

1) 52 ft	5) 54 m	9) 30 m^2
2) 26 in	6) 25 cm	10) 300 in^2
3) 112 ft	7) 38 in	11) 160 km^2
4) 20 cm	8) 24 m	12) 49 in^2

Trapezoids

1) 50 cm^2	4) 60 cm^2	7) 36
2) 105 m^2	5) 80	8) 15
3) 39 ft^2	6) 24	

Calculate

1) 13 cm	2) 11 ft	3) 12 m	4) 25 ft

Circles

1) 19.63 in^2	5) 379.94 cm^2	9) 12.56 m^2
2) 78.5 cm^2	6) 314 $miles^2$	10) 113.04 cm^2
3) 254.34 ft^2	7) 132.67 in^2	11) 38.47 $miles^2$
4) 12.56 m^2	8) 7.07 ft^2	12) 50.24 ft^2

Circle No.	Radius	Diameter	Circumference	Area
1	1 in	2 in	6.28 in	3.14 in^2
2	5 m	10 m	31.4 m	78.5 m^2
3	3 ft	6 ft	18.84 ft	28.26 ft^2
4	7.5 miles	15 mi	47.1 mi	176.63 mi^2
5	5.5 km	11 km	34.54 km	94.99 km^2
6	7 cm	14 cm	43.96 cm	153.86 cm^2
7	6 ft	12 ft	37.68 feet	113.04 ft^2
8	10 m	20 m	62.8 m	314 m^2
9	9 in	18 in	56.52 in	254.34 in^2
10	4.5 ft	9 ft	28.26 ft	63.585 ft^2

Cubes

1) 12
2) 8 cm^3
3) 216 ft^3
4) 1,331 m^3
5) 2,197 in^3

6) 343 $miles^3$
7) 1.728 km^3
8) 729 cm^3
9) 9.261 ft^3
10) 1,728 mm^3

11) 0.008 in^3
12) 0.001 km^3
13) 27
14) 294 m^2
15) 150 ft^2

16) 121.5 mm^2
17) 7.26 km^2
18) 726 cm^2

Rectangular Prism

1) 132 m^3
2) 800 in^3
3) 600 m^3

4) 112 cm^3
5) 288 ft^3
6) 420 m^3

7) 184 cm^2
8) 252 ft^2
9) 220 in^2

10) 438 m^2

Cylinder

1) 1,004.8 m^3
2) 214.6 cm^3
3) 9,495.4 cm^3

4) 1.1 m^3
5) 588.8 m^3
6) 452.2 in^3

7) 188.4 m^2
8) 602.9 cm^2
9) 37.7 cm^2

10) 401.9 m^2

Pyramids and Cone

1) 1,600 yd^3
2) 1,050 yd^3
3) 1,617 in^3

4) 392.5 m^3
5) 3,014.4 m^3
6) 366.33 cm^3

7) 1,440 yd^2
8) 1,536 m^2
9) 678.24 in^2

10) 1,205.76 cm^2

Chapter 16 :

Trigonometric Functions

Topics that you'll practice in this chapter:

- ✓ Trig ratios of General Angles
- ✓ Sketch Each Angle in Standard Position
- ✓ Finding Co–Terminal Angles and Reference Angles
- ✓ Angles in Radians
- ✓ Angles in Degrees
- ✓ Evaluating Each Trigonometric Expression
- ✓ Missing Sides and Angles of a Right Triangle
- ✓ Arc Length and Sector Area

Mathematics is like checkers in being suitable for the young, not too difficult, amusing, and without peril to the state. — *Plato*

Trig ratios of General Angles

✎ **Evaluate.**

1) $\sin 135° = $ _____

2) $\sin 300° = $ _____

3) $\cos -225° = $ _____

4) $\cos 270° = $ _____

5) $\sin 450° = $ _____

6) $\sin -330° = $ _____

7) $\tan 60° = $ _____

8) $\cot 180° = $ _____

9) $\tan 240° = $ _____

10) $\cot 90° = $ _____

11) $\sec 180° = $ _____

12) $\csc 90° = $ _____

13) $\cot -270° = $ _____

14) $\sec 360° = $ _____

15) $\cos -45° = $ _____

16) $\sec 120° = $ _____

17) $\csc 360° = $ _____

18) $\cot -45° = $ _____

✎ **Find the exact value of each trigonometric function. Some may be undefined.**

19) $\sec 2\pi = $ _____

20) $\tan -\dfrac{5\pi}{2} = $ _____

21) $\cos \dfrac{11\pi}{2} = $ _____

22) $\cot \dfrac{9\pi}{4} = $ _____

23) $\sec -6\pi = $ _____

24) $\sec \dfrac{\pi}{4} = $ _____

25) $\csc \dfrac{8\pi}{3} = $ _____

26) $\cot \dfrac{10\pi}{3} = $ _____

27) $\csc -\dfrac{\pi}{2} = $ _____

28) $\cot \dfrac{2\pi}{3} = $ _____

Sketch Each Angle in Standard Position

✎ **Draw each angle with the given measure in standard position.**

1) $-570°$

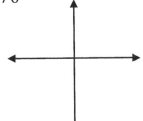

4) $-690°$

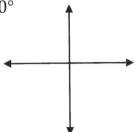

2) $750°$

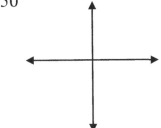

5) $\frac{13\pi}{6}$

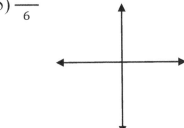

3) $1,110°$

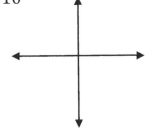

6) $-\frac{11\pi}{6}$

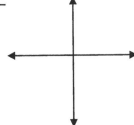

Finding Co-terminal Angles and Reference Angles

✍ **Find a conterminal angle between 0° and 360° for each angle provided.**

1) $-315° =$

3) $-225° =$

2) $-210° =$

4) $-540° =$

✍ **Find a conterminal angle between 0 and 2π for each given angle.**

5) $\dfrac{18\pi}{5} =$

7) $-\dfrac{13\pi}{4} =$

6) $-\dfrac{19\pi}{6} =$

8) $\dfrac{14\pi}{3} =$

✍ **Find the reference angle of each angle.**

9)

10)

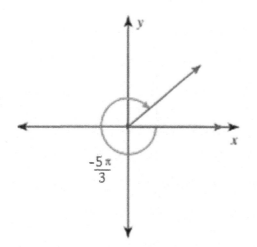

$\dfrac{-5\pi}{3}$

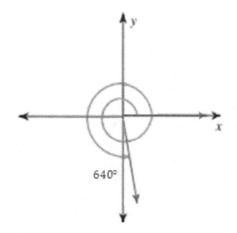

$640°$

Angles and Angle Measure

✎ **Convert each degree measure into radians.**

1) $216° =$ ___

2) $660° =$ ___

3) $420° =$ ___

4) $220° =$ ___

5) $210° =$ ___

6) $270° =$ ___

7) $-300° =$ ___

8) $810° =$ ___

9) $330° =$ ___

10) $140° =$ ___

11) $480° =$ ___

12) $405° =$ ___

13) $-450° =$ ___

14) $-126° =$ ___

15) $-675° =$ ___

16) $150° =$ ___

17) $-468° =$ ___

18) $340° =$ ___

19) $-440° =$ ___

20) $342° =$ ___

21) $230° =$ ___

✎ **Convert each radian measure into degrees.**

22) $\dfrac{\pi}{10} =$

23) $\dfrac{5\pi}{12} =$

24) $\dfrac{7\pi}{3} =$

25) $\dfrac{3\pi}{20} =$

26) $-\dfrac{6\pi}{5} =$

27) $\dfrac{11\pi}{18} =$

28) $-\dfrac{14\pi}{5} =$

29) $\dfrac{5\pi}{18} =$

30) $\dfrac{7\pi}{36} =$

31) $\dfrac{17\pi}{18} =$

32) $-\dfrac{13\pi}{30} =$

33) $\dfrac{7\pi}{9} =$

34) $-\dfrac{19\pi}{18} =$

35) $\dfrac{7\pi}{60} =$

36) $-\dfrac{3\pi}{10} =$

37) $\dfrac{11\pi}{30} =$

38) $-\dfrac{2\pi}{9} =$

39) $-\dfrac{7\pi}{10} =$

Evaluating Trigonometric Functions

✍ **Find the exact value of each trigonometric function.**

1) $\cos 780° = $ _____

2) $\tan \dfrac{5\pi}{3} = $ _____

3) $\tan -\dfrac{\pi}{6} = $ _____

4) $\cot -\dfrac{9\pi}{4} = $ _____

5) $\cos -\dfrac{7\pi}{6} = $ _____

6) $\cos 135° = $ _____

7) $\sin 240° = $ _____

8) $\tan 330° = $ _____

9) $\cot 420° = $ _____

10) $\tan - 495° = $ _____

11) $\cot 315° = $ _____

12) $\sin - 240° = $ _____

13) $\cot 225° = $ _____

✍ **Use the given point on the terminal side of angle θ to find the value of the trigonometric function indicated.**

14) $\sin\theta,\ (-6, 8)$

15) $\cos\theta,\ (-6, 8)$

16) $\sec\theta,\ (3,\ 5)$

17) $\cos\theta,\ (10, 24)$

18) $\sin\theta,\ (6, -6)$

19) $\tan\theta,\ (-2, -\sqrt{12})$

Missing Sides and Angles of a Right Triangle

✎ Find the value of each trigonometric ratio as fractions in their simplest form.

1) $cot\ x$

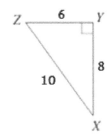

2) $cos\ A$

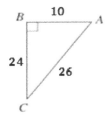

✎ Find the missing sides. Round answers to the nearest tenth.

3)

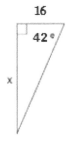

4)

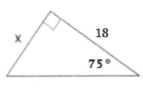

5)

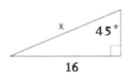

6)

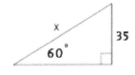

Arc Length and Sector Area

✎ **Find the length of each arc. Round your answers to the nearest tenth.**

($\pi = 3.14$)

1) $r = 28$ cm, $\theta = 30°$

3) $r = 22$ ft, $\theta = 50°$

2) $r = 14$ ft, $\theta = 95°$

4) $r = 16$ m, $\theta = 85°$

✎ **Find area of each sector. Do *not* round. Round your answers to the nearest tenth.** ($\pi = 3.14$)

5)

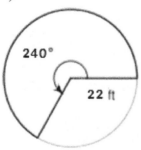

7)

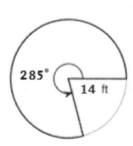

6)

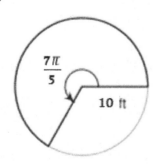

8)

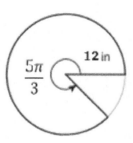

Answers of Worksheets

Trig Ratios of General Angles

1) $\frac{\sqrt{2}}{2}$

2) $-\frac{\sqrt{3}}{2}$

3) $-\frac{\sqrt{2}}{2}$

4) 0

5) 1

6) $\frac{1}{2}$

7) $\sqrt{3}$

8) Undefined

9) $\sqrt{3}$

10) 0

11) -1

12) 1

13) 0

14) 1

15) $\frac{\sqrt{2}}{2}$

16) -2

17) Undefined

18) -1

19) 1

20) Undefined

21) 0

22) 1

23) 1

24) $\sqrt{2}$

25) $\frac{2\sqrt{3}}{3}$

26) $\frac{\sqrt{3}}{3}$

27) -1

28) $-\frac{\sqrt{3}}{3}$

Sketch Each Angle in Standard Position

1) $-570°$

2) $750°$

3) $1,110°$

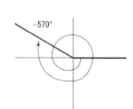

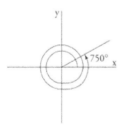

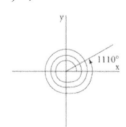

4) $-690°$

5) $\frac{13\pi}{6} = 390°$

6) $-\frac{11\pi}{6} = -330°$

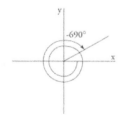

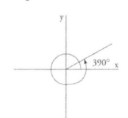

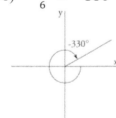

Finding Co–Terminal Angles and Reference Angles

1) $45°$

2) $150°$

3) $135°$

4) $180°$

5) $\frac{4\pi}{5}$

6) $\frac{5\pi}{6}$

7) $\frac{3\pi}{4}$

8) $\frac{2\pi}{3}$

9) $\frac{\pi}{3}$

10) $80°$

Angles and Angle Measure

1) $\frac{6\pi}{5}$

2) $\frac{11\pi}{3}$

3) $\frac{7\pi}{3}$

4) $\frac{11\pi}{9}$

5) $\frac{7\pi}{6}$

6) $\frac{3\pi}{2}$

7) $-\frac{5\pi}{3}$

8) $\frac{9\pi}{2}$

9) $\frac{11\pi}{6}$

10) $\frac{7\pi}{9}$

11) $\frac{8\pi}{3}$

12) $\frac{9\pi}{4}$

13) $-\frac{5}{2}\pi$

14) $-\frac{7\pi}{10}$

15) $-\frac{15\pi}{4}$

16) $\frac{5\pi}{6}$

17) $-\frac{13\pi}{5}$

18) $\frac{17\pi}{9}$

19) $-\frac{22\pi}{9}$

20) $\frac{19\pi}{10}$

21) $\frac{23\pi}{18}$

22) $18°$

23) $75°$

24) $420°$

25) $27°$

26) $-216°$

27) $110°$

28) $-504°$

29) $50°$

30) $35°$

31) $170°$

32) $-78°$

33) $140°$

34) $-190°$

35) $21°$

36) $-54°$

37) $66°$

38) $-40°$

39) $-126°$

Evaluating Each Trigonometric Functions

1) $\frac{1}{2}$

2) $-\sqrt{3}$

3) $-\frac{\sqrt{3}}{3}$

4) -1

5) $-\frac{\sqrt{3}}{2}$

6) $-\frac{\sqrt{2}}{2}$

7) $-\frac{\sqrt{3}}{2}$

8) $-\frac{\sqrt{3}}{3}$

9) $\frac{\sqrt{3}}{3}$

10) 1

11) -1

12) $\frac{\sqrt{3}}{2}$

13) 1

14) 0.8

15) -0.6

16) $\frac{\sqrt{34}}{5}$

17) $\frac{5}{13}$

18) $-\frac{\sqrt{2}}{2}$

19) $\sqrt{3}$

Missing Sides and Angles of a Right Triangle

1) $\frac{4}{3}$

2) $\frac{5}{13}$

3) 14.4

4) 67.2

5) 22.6

6) 40.4

Arc Length and Sector Area

1) $14.7 \, cm$

2) $23.2 \, ft$

3) $19.2 \, ft$

4) $23.7m$

5) $1,013.7 \, ft^2$

6) $220 \, in^2$

7) $487.5 \, ft^2$

8) $377 \, in^2$

Chapter 17 :

ALEKS Math Test Review

ALEKS (Assessment and Learning in Knowledge Spaces) is an artificial intelligence-based assessment tool to measure students' mathematical knowledge to place students in the most appropriate level for their current math skills.

ALEKS test consists 20 to 35 open-ended questions covering a variety of math topics and there's no time limit on the test, so you can focus on doing your best to demonstrate your skills.

ALEKS uses a computer–adaptive technology and the questions you see are based on your skill level. Your response to each question drives the difficulty level of the next question.

ALEKS does NOT permit the use of personal calculators on the placement test. The test expects students to be able to answer certain questions without the assistance of a calculator. Therefore, they provide an onscreen calculator for students to use on some questions.

In this section, there are two complete ALEKS Mathematics Placement Assessment Tests.

Take these tests to see what score you'll be able to receive on a real ALEKS test.

The hardest arithmetic to master is that which enables us to count our blessings.
   -Eric Hoffer

Time to Test

Time to refine your skill with a practice examination.

Take a practice ALEKS Math Test to simulate the test day experience. After you've finished, score your test using the answer key.

Before You Start

- You'll need a pencil, a calculator and a timer to take the test.

- After you've finished the test, review the answer key to see where you went wrong.

Good Luck!

ALEKS Math Practice Test Answer Sheets

Remove (or photocopy) these answer sheets and use them to complete the practice tests.

ALEKS Practice Test

1		21	
2		22	
3		23	
4		24	
5		25	
6		26	
7		27	
8		28	
9		29	
10		30	
11		31	
12		32	
13		33	
14		34	
15		35	
16			
17			
18			
19			
20			

ALEKS Math Practice Test 1

Mathematics Placement Assessment

❖ **35 Questions.**

❖ **Total time for this test: No Limit Time.**

❖ **You may NOT use a calculator on this Section.**

Administered *Month Year*

1) If x is a positive integer divisible by 6, and $x < 50$, what is the greatest possible value of x?

48

$6 \times 8 =$

2) If $a = 6$, what is the value of b in this equation?

$b = 12$

$$b = \frac{a^2}{6} + 6$$

3) One fourth of 32 is equal to $\frac{2}{5}$ of what number?

$8 = \frac{2}{5}x$ $x = 20$

$40 = 2x$.

$32 = \frac{2}{5}x$ $x = 80$

$160 = 2x$

4) $(p^4) \times (p^6) = p^{10}$

$50 + 45 + 3$

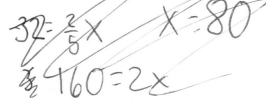

5) Simplify: $5 - \frac{4}{7}x \geq 33$

-28

$28 \times 7 \div 4 \geq x$

$98 \geq x$ $-49 \geq x$

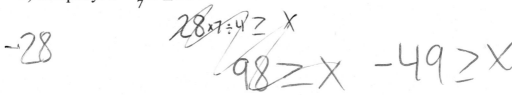

6) A soccer team played 160 games and won 30 percent of them. How many games did the team win?

$160 \times .3 =$

48 games

7) What is a common factor of both $x^2 - 3x - 18$ and $x^2 - 8x + 12$?

$(x-6)(x+3)$ $(x-6)(x-2)$

$(x-6)$

8) The ratio of boys to girls in a school is 5:4. If there are 720 students in a school, how many boys are in the school.

$720 \cdot \frac{5}{4}$

$\frac{720 \cdot 5}{9} = $ 400

3600

280
+ 80
360

1800 ÷ 2

900

9) What is the area of an isosceles right triangle that has one leg that measures 8 cm?

$\frac{8 \times 8}{2} = 32$

10) $(x + 7)(x + 5) = x^2 + 12x + 35$

11) $\frac{1}{2b^2} + \frac{1}{7b} = \frac{1}{b^2}$, then $b =$?

$\frac{7b}{14b^3} + \frac{2b^2}{14b^3} = \frac{1}{b^2}$ $2b^2 + 7b = b^2$

$b^2 + 7b = 0$

$b + 7 = 0$

$7b + 2b^2 = 14b$

$2b^2 = 7b$

$b = -7$ $b = \frac{7}{2}b = 3.5$

12) If two angles in a triangle measure 61 degrees and 49 degrees, what is the value of the third angle?

$70°$

180
$- 49$
131
$- 61$
70

13) $7^{\frac{8}{5}} \times 7^{\frac{2}{5}} =?$ $7^2 = 49$

14) What is 472.3571 rounded to the nearest hundredth?

472.36

15) $x^2 - 169 = 0$, What is (are) the value of x?

$(x+13)(x-13)$ $X = 13, -13$

16) If $a = 3$ what's the value of $2a^2 + 3a + 5$?

$18 + 9 + 5$

32

17) Sophia purchased a sofa for $297.60. The sofa is regularly priced at $465.

What was the percent discount Sophia received on the sofa?

$297.6 X = 465$

56% $X = 1.56$

$100 - 64 = 36\%$

18) The average of eight consecutive numbers is 42. What is the smallest

number? $39, 40, 41, 42, 43, 44, 45 \ell$

$8X = \frac{42}{8}$

19) The sum of four numbers is 42. If another number is added to these four numbers, the average of the five numbers is 22. What is the fifth number?

20) If $f(x) = 2 + 4x$ and $g(x) = 3x^2 - 7 - 5x$, then find $(g - f)(x)$?

$3x^2 - 9x - 9$

21) David owed $6,248. After making 41 payments of $112 each, how much did he have left to pay?

$$\begin{array}{r} 62\overset{4}{4}\overset{3}{8} \\ -\ 45\ 9\overset{}{2} \\ \hline 1658 \end{array}$$

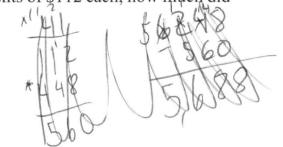

22) Simplify the following inequality.

$\frac{|3 + x|}{8} \le 4$

$|3 + x| \le 4 \times 8$

23) $\sin\left(-\frac{2\pi}{3}\right) = ?$

24) $\dfrac{\sqrt{32a^7b^3}}{\sqrt{2a^2b}} = ?$

25) Find the slope–intercept form of the graph $4x - 7y = -15$

26) What are the zeros of the function: $f(x) = x^3 + 5x^2 - 24x$?

27) The cost, in thousands of dollars, of producing x thousands of textbooks is C $(x) = x^2 + 4x + 15$. The revenue, also in thousands of dollars, is R $(x) = 6x$. Find the profit or loss if 3,000 textbooks are produced. (profit = revenue – cost)

28) Suppose a triangle has the dimensions indicated below; Then cos B =?

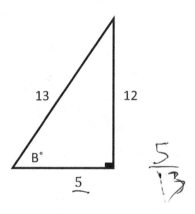

$$\frac{5}{13}$$

29) What is the solution of the following system of equations?

$$X = -1$$
$$Y = 1$$

$$\begin{cases} x + 3y = 2 \\ 5x - 4y = -9 \end{cases}$$

$$-19y = -19$$

$$-15y + 10 - 4y = -9 \qquad y = 1$$

30) Find the Center and Radius of the graph $(x - 2)^2 + (y + 5)^2 = 32$

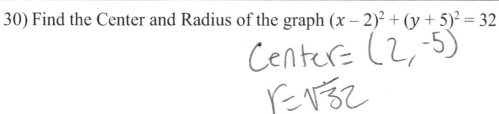

Center = $(2, -5)$

$r = \sqrt{32}$

31) Simplify $\dfrac{7 - 3i}{-7i}$

32) What is the domain of the following function? $f(x) = \sqrt{x - 5} + 14$

33) Find the inverse function of $f(x) = \dfrac{3x - 18}{6}$

34) What is the value of x in the following equation?

$\log (x + 5) - \log (x - 4) = 1$

35) A number is chosen at random from 1 to 10. Find the probability of not selecting a composite number.

"The End of Test 1"

ALEKS Math Practice Test 2

Mathematics Placement Assessment

❖ **35 Questions.**

❖ **Total time for this test: No Limit Time.**

❖ **You may NOT use a calculator on this Section.**

Administered *Month Year*

1) Write the $\frac{7}{140}$ as a decimal.

2) $5 + 4 \times (-2) - [6 + 27 \times 2] \div 3 =?$

3) If $5 + 6x \le 53$, what is the value of $x \le$?

4) Simplify. $\dfrac{\frac{1}{2} - \frac{x+3}{4}}{\frac{x^2}{2} - \frac{9}{2}}$

5) A man owed \$1,979 on his car. After making 32 payments of \$39 each, how much did he have left to pay?

6) Find the solutions of the following equation.

$$4x^2 + 8x - 16 = 0$$

7) How many 8×8 squares can fit inside a rectangle with a height of 48 and width of 32?

8) $(x^4)^{\frac{5}{8}} = ?$

9) What is 4,198.476587 rounded to the nearest tenth?

10) Last Friday Jacob had $35.38. Over the weekend he received some money for cleaning the attic. He now has $68. How much money did he receive?

11) 42 is what percent of 60?

12) Liam's average (arithmetic mean) on three mathematics tests is 14. What should Liam's score be on the next test to have an overall of 15 for all the tests?

13) Find all values of x in this equation: $3x^2 + 8x + 4 = 0$

14) What is the value of x in this equation? $6^7 \times 6^6 = 6^x$

15) In the following triangle what is the value of x?

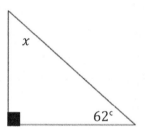

16) Find the factors of $x^2 + 4x - 21$.

17) If a vehicle is driven 45 miles on Monday, 57 miles on Tuesday, and 39 miles on Wednesday, what is the average number of miles driven each day?

18) A ladder leans against a wall forming a 60° angle between the ground and the ladder. If the bottom of the ladder is 40 feet away from the wall, how long is the ladder?

19) What is the distance between the points $(3, -2)$ and $(6, 2)$?

20) $(x - 4)(3x^2 + 7x + 2) = ?$

21) What is the value of $\sin 60\circ$?

22) If θ is an acute angle and $\cos \theta = \dfrac{4}{5}$ then $\sin \theta = ?$

23) If $\log_3 x = 4$, then $x = ?$

24) If $f(x) = x - \dfrac{8}{3}$ and f^{-1} is the inverse of $f(x)$, what is the value of $f^{-1}(2)$?

25) Solve. $|18 - (54 \div |1 - 7|)| = ?$

26) What's the reciprocal of $\frac{x^7}{25}$?

27) What is the solution of the following system of equations?

$$\begin{cases} -2x + y = 5 \\ 5x + 4y = -6 \end{cases}$$

28) What is the equivalent temperature of 68°F in Celsius?

$$C = \frac{5}{9}(F - 32)$$

29) Simplify $(-3 + 4i)(2 + 5i)$.

30) Find $\tan \frac{4\pi}{6}$.

31) If $f(x) = 9x - 36$ and $g(x) = 3x^2 - 12x$, then find $(\frac{f}{g})(x)$.

32) What is the center and radius of a circle with the following equation?

$$(x - 4)^2 + (y + 5)^2 = 10$$

33) If the center of a circle is at the point $(-2, 3)$ and its circumference equals to 8π, what is the standard form equation of the circle?

34) Anita's trick–or–treat bag contains 23 pieces of chocolate, 20 suckers, 12 pieces of gum, 25 pieces of licorice. If she randomly pulls a piece of candy from her bag, what is the probability of her pulling out a piece of sucker?

35) What is the value of x in the following equation?

$$\log_5(x + 3) - \log_5(x - 3) = 1$$

"The End of Test 2"

Chapter 18 :
Answers and Explanations

Answer Key

✳ Now, it's time to review your results to see where you went wrong and what areas you need to improve!

ALEKS Math Practice Test

Practice Test 1				Practice Test 2			
1	48	21	1,656	1	0.05	21	$\frac{\sqrt{3}}{2}$
2	12	22	$-35 \le x \le 29$	2	-23	22	$\frac{3}{5}$
3	20	23	$-\frac{\sqrt{3}}{2}$	3	$x \le 8$	23	81
4	P^{10}	24	$4a^2b\sqrt{a}$	4	$-\frac{x+1}{2(x^2-9)}$	24	$\frac{14}{3}$
5	$x \le -49$	25	$\frac{4}{7}$	5	731	25	9
6	48	26	$0, 3, -8$	6	$-1 \pm \sqrt{5}$	26	$\frac{25}{x^5}$
7	$(x-6)$	27	18,000 loss	7	24	27	$(-2,1)$
8	400	28	$\frac{5}{13}$	8	$x^{\frac{5}{2}}$	28	20
9	32	29	$(-1,1)$	9	4,198.5	29	$-7i - 26$
10	$x^2 + 12x + 35$			10	32.62	30	$-\sqrt{3}$
11	3.5	30	$(2,-5), 4\sqrt{2}$	11	70	31	$\frac{3}{x}$
12	70°	31	$\frac{3}{7} + i$	12	18	32	$(4,-5), \sqrt{10}$
13	7^2	32	$[5, +\infty)$	13	$(-2, -\frac{2}{3})$	33	***
14	472.36	33	$2(x+3)$	14	9^{13}	34	$\frac{1}{4}$
15	± 13	34	5	15	28°	35	$4\frac{1}{2}$
16	32	35	$\frac{1}{2}$	16	$(x-3)(x+7)$		
17	36%			17	47		
18	34.5			18	80		$***(x+2)^2 + (y-3)^2 = 4^2$
19	68			19	5		
20	$3x^2 - 9x - 9$			20	$3x^3 - 5x^2 - 26x - 8$		

Answers and Explanations

ALEKS Mathematics Placement Assessment

Practice Tests 1

1) Answer: 48.

$\frac{30}{6} = 5, \frac{42}{6} = 7, \frac{48}{6} = 8$; 49 not divisible by 6.

2) Answer: 12.

If $a = 6$ then $b = \frac{6^2}{6} + 6 \Rightarrow b = \frac{36}{6} + 6 \Rightarrow b = 6 + 6 = 12$

3) Answer: 20.

Let x be the number. Write the equation and solve for x.

$\frac{1}{4} \times 32 = \frac{2}{5} \times x \Rightarrow \frac{1 \times 32}{4} = \frac{2x}{5}$, use cross multiplication to solve for x.

$5 \times 32 = 2x \times 4 \Rightarrow 160 = 8x \Rightarrow x = 20$

4) Answer: P^{10}.

$(p^4) \times (p^6) = p^{4+6} = p^{10}$

5) Answer: $x \leq -49$.

$5 - \frac{4}{7}x \geq 33 \Rightarrow -\frac{4}{7}x \geq 28 \Rightarrow -x \geq 49 \Rightarrow x \leq -49$

6) Answer: 48.

$160 \times \frac{30}{100} = 48$

7) Answer: $(x - 6)$.

Factor each trinomial $x^2 - 3x - 18$ and $x^2 - 8x + 12$

$x^2 - 3x - 18 \Rightarrow (x - 6)(x + 3)$

$x^2 - 8x + 12 \Rightarrow (x - 2)(x - 6) \Rightarrow$ The common Factor is: $(x - 6)$

8) Answer: 400.

The ratio of boy to girls is 5:4. Therefore, there are 5 boys out of 9 students. To find the answer, first divide the total number of students by 9, then multiply the result by 5.

$720 \div 9 = 80 \Rightarrow 80 \times 5 = 400$

9) Answer: 32.

$a = 8 \Rightarrow$ area of triangle is $= \frac{1}{2}(8 \times 8) = \frac{64}{2} = 32 \text{ cm}^2$

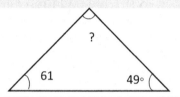

Isosceles right triangle

10) Answer: $x^2 + 12x + 35$.

Use FOIL (First, Out, In, Last)

$(x + 7)(x + 5) = x^2 + 5x + 7x + 35 = x^2 + 12x + 35$

11) Answer: 3.5.

$\frac{7+2b}{14b^2} = \frac{1}{b^2} \Rightarrow (b \neq 0) \; b^2(7 + 2b) = 14b^2 \Rightarrow 7 + 2b = 14 \Rightarrow 2b = 7 \Rightarrow b = 3.5$

12) Answer: 70°

$61° + 49° = 110°$

$180° - 110° = 70°$

The value of the third angle is 70°.

13) Answer: 7^2.

$7^{\frac{8}{5}} \times 7^{\frac{2}{5}} = 7^{\frac{8}{5}+\frac{2}{5}} = 7^{\frac{10}{5}} = 7^2$

14) Answer: 472.36.

Underline the hundredths place: 472.3$\underline{5}$71

Look to the right if it is 5 or bigger, add it by 1.

Then, round up to 472.36

15) Answer: ±13.

$x^2 - 169 = 0 \Rightarrow x^2 = 169 \Rightarrow x = 13$ or $x = -13$

16) Answer: 32.

If $a = 3$, then:

$2a^2 + 3a + 5 \Rightarrow 2(3)^2 + 3(3) + 5 \Rightarrow 2(9) + 9 + 5 = 32$

17) Answer: 36%.

The question is this: 297.60 is what percent of 465?

Use percent formula: part $= \frac{\text{percent}}{100} \times$ whole

$297.60 = \frac{\text{percent}}{100} \times 465 \Rightarrow 297.60 = \frac{\text{percent} \times 465}{100} \Rightarrow 29{,}760 = \text{percent} \times 465$

$$\Rightarrow \text{percent} = \frac{29{,}760}{465} = 64$$

297.60 is 64 % of 465. Therefore, the discount is: 100% – 64% = 36%

18) **Answer: 34.5.**

Let x be the smallest number. Then, these are the numbers:

$x, x + 1, x + 2, x + 3 , x + 4, x + 5, x + 6, x + 7$

$$\text{average} = \frac{\text{sum of terms}}{\text{number of terms}} \Rightarrow 42 = \frac{x+(x+1)+(x+2)+(x+3)+(x+4)+(x+5)+(x+6))+(x+7)}{7} \Rightarrow 304 =$$

$8x + 28 \Rightarrow 276 = 8x \Rightarrow x = 34.5$

19) **Answer: 68.**

$a + b + c + d = 42$

$\frac{a+b+c+d+e}{5} = 22 \Rightarrow a + b + c + d + e = 110 \Rightarrow 42 + e = 110$

$e = 110 - 42 = 68$

20) **Answer: $3x^2 - 9x - 9$.**

$(g - f)(x) = g(x) - f(x) = (3x^2 - 7 - 5x) - (2 + 4x))$

$3x^2 - 7 - 5x - 2 - 4x = 3x^2 - 9x - 9$

21) **Answer: 1,656.**

$41 \times \$112 = \$4{,}592$; Payable amount is: $\$6{,}248 - \$4{,}592 = \$1{,}656$

22) **Answer: $-35 \le x \le 29$.**

$\frac{|3+x|}{8} \le 4 \Rightarrow |3 + x| \le 32 \Rightarrow -32 \le 3 + x \le 32 \Rightarrow -32 - 3 \le x \le 32 - 3 \Rightarrow$

$-35 \le x \le 29$

23) **Answer: $-\frac{\sqrt{3}}{2}$.**

$\sin\left(-\frac{2\pi}{3}\right) = -\frac{\sqrt{3}}{2}$

24) **Answer: $4a^2 b\sqrt{a}$.**

$\frac{\sqrt{32a^7 b^3}}{\sqrt{2a^2 b}} = \frac{4a^3 b\sqrt{2ab}}{a\sqrt{2b}} = 4a^2 b\sqrt{a}$

25) **Answer: $\frac{4}{7}$.**

$-7y = -4x - 15 \Rightarrow y = \frac{-4}{-7}x - \frac{15}{-7} \Rightarrow y = \frac{4}{7}x + \frac{15}{7}$

26) Answer: 0, 3, −8.

Frist factor the function:

$x(x-3)(x+8)$

To find the zeros, $f(x)$ **should be zero.**

$f(x) = x(x-3)(x+8) = 0$

Therefore, the zeros **are:** $x = 0$

$(x-3) = 0 \Rightarrow x = 3$

$(x+8) = 0 \Rightarrow x = -8$

27) Answer: 18,000loss.

$c(3) = (3)^2 + 4(3) + 15 = 9 + 12 + 15 = 36$

$6 \times 3 = 18 \Rightarrow 18 - 36 = -18 \Rightarrow 18,000\text{loss}$

28) Answer: $\frac{5}{13}$.

$\cos B = \dfrac{5}{13}$

29) Answer: $(-1, 1)$.

$\begin{cases} -5(x + 3y = 2) \\ 5x - 4y = -9 \end{cases}$ $\Rightarrow$ Multiply the first equation by $-5 \Rightarrow \begin{cases} -5x - 15y = -10 \\ 5x - 4y = -9 \end{cases}$

Add two equations $\Rightarrow -19y = -19 \Rightarrow y = 1$ then: $x = -1$

30) Answer: $(2, -5), 4\sqrt{2}$.

$(x - h)^2 + (y - k)^2 = r^2 \Rightarrow$ center: (h, k) and radius: r

$(x - 2)^2 + (y + 5)^2 = 32 \Rightarrow$ center: $(2, -5)$ and radius: $4\sqrt{2}$

31) Answer: $\frac{3}{7} + i$.

$\dfrac{7 - 3i}{-7i} \times \dfrac{i}{i} = \dfrac{7i - 3i^2}{-7i^2} = \dfrac{7i - 3(-1)}{-7(-1)} = \dfrac{3}{7} + i$

32) Answer: $[5, +\infty)$

The number under the square root symbol must be zero or greater than zero therefore:

$x - 5 \geq 0 \Rightarrow x \geq 5$; domain of function $= [5, +\infty)$

33) Answer: $2(x + 3)$.

$$f(x) = \frac{3x - 18}{6} \Rightarrow y = \frac{3x - 18}{6} \Rightarrow 6y = 3x - 18 \Rightarrow 6y + 18 = 3x \Rightarrow 2y + 6 = x$$

$$f^{-1} = 2x + 6 = 2(x + 3)$$

34) Answer: 5.

<u>METHOD ONE:</u>

$\log(x + 5) - \log(x - 4) = 1$, Add $\log(x - 4)$ to both sides:

$\log(x + 5) - \log(x - 4) + \log(x - 4) = 1 + \log(x - 4)$

And simplify: $\log(x + 5) = 1 + \log(x - 4)$

Logarithm rule: $a = \log_b(b^a) \Rightarrow 1 = \log_{10}(10^1) = \log(10)$

then: $\log(x + 5) = \log(10) + \log(x - 4)$

Logarithm rule: $\log_c(a) + \log_c(b) = \log_c(ab)$

then: $\log(10) + \log(x - 4) = \log(10(x - 4))$

$\log(x + 5) = \log(10(x - 4))$

When the logs have the same base:

$\log_b(f(x)) = \log_b(g(x)) \Rightarrow f(x) = g(x)$

$x + 5 = 10(x - 4) \Rightarrow x + 5 = 10x - 40 \Rightarrow 9x = 45 \Rightarrow x = 5$

<u>METHOD TWO</u>

We know that: $\log_a b - \log_a c = \log_a \frac{b}{c}$, and $\log b = c \Rightarrow b = 10^c$

Then, $\log(x + 5) - \log(x - 4) = \log \frac{x+5}{x-4} = 1 \Rightarrow \frac{x+5}{x-4} = 10^1 \Rightarrow x + 5 = 10(x - 4) \Rightarrow$

$x + 5 = 10x - 40 \Rightarrow 10x - x = 5 + 40 \Rightarrow x = 5$

35) Answer: $\frac{1}{2}$.

Set of number that are not composite between 1 and 10: A= {1, 2, 3, 5, 7}

$$n(A) = 5 \Rightarrow p = \frac{5}{10} = \frac{1}{2}$$

Answers and Explanations

ALEKS Mathematics Placement Assessment

Practice Tests 2

1) Answer: 0.05.

$$\frac{7}{140} = \frac{1}{20} = 0.05$$

2) Answer: −23.

Use PEMDAS (order of operation):

$$5 + 4 \times (-2) - [6 + 27 \times 2] \div 3 = 5 + (-8) - [6 + 54] \div 3 = -3 - 60 \div 3 = -3 - 20 = -23$$

3) Answer: $x \le 8$.

$$5 + 6x \le 53 \Rightarrow 6x \le 53 - 5 \Rightarrow 6x \le 48 \Rightarrow x \le 8$$

4) Answer: $-\dfrac{x+1}{2(x^2-9)}$.

Simplify: $\dfrac{\frac{1}{2} - \frac{x+3}{4}}{\frac{x^2}{2} - \frac{9}{2}} = \dfrac{\frac{1}{2} - \frac{x+3}{4}}{\frac{x^2-9}{2}} = \dfrac{2(\frac{1}{2} - \frac{x+3}{4})}{x^2-9} \Rightarrow$ Simplify: $\dfrac{1}{2} - \dfrac{x+3}{4} = \dfrac{-x-1}{4}$

then: $\dfrac{\frac{1}{2} - \frac{x+3}{4}}{\frac{x^2}{2} - \frac{9}{2}} = \dfrac{2(\frac{1}{2} - \frac{x+3}{4})}{x^2-9} = \dfrac{\frac{-x-1}{2}}{x^2-9} = \dfrac{-x-1}{2(x^2-9)} = -\dfrac{x+1}{2x^2-18}$

5) Answer: $731.

$32 \times \$39 = \$1,248$ Payable amount is: $\$1,979 - \$1,248 = \$731$

6) Answer: $-1 \pm \sqrt{5}$.

$$x_{1,2} = \frac{-b \pm \sqrt{b^2 - 4ac}}{2a}$$

$ax^2 + bx + c = 0 \Rightarrow 4x^2 + 8x - 16 = 0$, then: a = 4, b = 8 and c = −16

$$x_1 = \frac{-8 + \sqrt{8^2 - 4 \times 8 \times (-16)}}{2 \times 4} = \sqrt{5} - 1 \; ; \; x_2 = \frac{-8 - \sqrt{8^2 - 4 \times 8 \times (-16)}}{2 \times 4} = -1 - \sqrt{5}$$

7) Answer: 24.

Number of squares equal to: $\dfrac{48 \times 32}{8 \times 8} = 6 \times 4 = 24$

8) Answer: $x^{\frac{5}{2}}$.

$$(x^4)^{\frac{5}{8}} = x^{4 \times \frac{5}{8}} = x^{\frac{20}{8}} = x^{\frac{5}{2}}$$

9) Answer: 4,198.5.

Underline the tenth place: 4,198.476587

Look to the right if it is 5 or bigger, add 1 to the underlined digit.

Then, round up the decimal to 4,198.5

10) Answer: $32.62.

$68 - $35.38 = $32.62

11) Answer: 70.

$60 \times \dfrac{x}{100} = 42 \Rightarrow 60 \times x = 4,200 \Rightarrow x = \dfrac{4,200}{60} = 70$

12) Answer: 18.

$\dfrac{a + b + c}{3} = 14 \Rightarrow a + b + c = 42$

$\dfrac{a + b + c + d}{4} = 15 \Rightarrow a + b + c + d = 60$

$42 + c = 60 \Rightarrow c = 60 - 42 = 18$

13) Answer: $-2, -\dfrac{2}{3}$.

$x_{1,2} = \dfrac{-b \pm \sqrt{b^2 - 4ac}}{2a}$

$ax^2 + bx + c = 0;\ 3x^2 + 8x + 4 = 0 \Rightarrow$ then: a = 3, b = 8 and c = 4

$x_1 = \dfrac{-8 - \sqrt{8^2 - 4 \times 3 \times 4}}{2 \times 3} = -2$

$x_2 = \dfrac{-8 + \sqrt{8^2 - 4 \times 3 \times 4}}{2 \times 3} = -\dfrac{2}{3}$

14) Answer: 9^{13}.

$6^7 \times 6^6 = 6^{7+6} = 6^{13}$

15) Answer: 28°.

$90° + 62° = 152°$

$180° - 152° = 28°$

16) Answer: $(x - 3)(x + 7)$.

$x^2 + 4x - 21 = (x - 3)(x + 7)$

17) Answer: 47.

$45 + 57 + 39 = 141 \Rightarrow$ Average $= \dfrac{141}{3} = 47$

18) **Answer: 80.**

The relationship among all sides of special right triangle

$30°, 60°, 90°$ is provided in this triangle:

In this triangle, the opposite side of $30°$ angle is half of the hypotenuse.

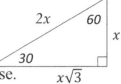

Draw the shape of this question:

The latter is the hypotenuse. Therefore, the latter is 80 ft.

19) **Answer: 5.**

$C = \sqrt{(x_A - x_B)^2 + (y_A - y_B)^2}$

$C = \sqrt{(3 - (6))^2 + (-2 - 2)^2}$

$C = \sqrt{(-3)^2 + (-4)^2} \Rightarrow C = \sqrt{9 + 16} \Rightarrow C = \sqrt{25} = 5$

20) **Answer: $3x^3 - 5x^2 - 26x - 8$.**

Use FOIL (First, Out, In, Last)

$(x - 4)(3x^2 + 7x + 2) = 3x^3 + 7x^2 + 2x - 12x^2 - 28x - 8$

$= 3x^3 - 5x^2 - 26x - 8$

21) **Answer: $\frac{\sqrt{3}}{2}$.**

$sin\ 60° = \frac{\sqrt{3}}{2}$

22) **Answer: $\frac{3}{5}$.**

$COS\theta = \frac{4}{5} \Rightarrow$ we have following triangle, then

$c = \sqrt{5^2 - 4^2} = \sqrt{25 - 16} = \sqrt{9} = 3$

$sin\theta = \frac{3}{5}$

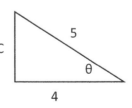

23) **Answer: 81.**

<u>**METHOD ONE:**</u>

$log_3 x = 4$

Apply logarithm rule: $a = log_b(b^a)$

$4 = \log_3(3^4) = \log_3(81)$

$\log_3 x = \log_3(81)$

When the logs have the same base:

$\log_b(f(x)) = \log_b(g(x)) \Rightarrow f(x) = g(x)$

then: $x = 81$

METHOD TWO:

We know that: $\log_a b = c \Rightarrow b = a^c \Rightarrow \log_3 x = 4 \Rightarrow x = 3^4 = 81$

24) **Answer:** $\frac{14}{3}$.

$f(x) = x - \frac{8}{3} \Rightarrow y = x - \frac{8}{3} \Rightarrow y + \frac{8}{3} = x$

$f^{-1}(x) = x + \frac{8}{3} \Longrightarrow f^{-1}(2) = 2 + \frac{8}{3} = \frac{14}{3}$

25) **Answer: 9.**

$|18 - (54 \div |1 - 7|)| = |18 - (54 \div |-6|)| = |18 - (54 \div 6)| = |18 - 9| = |9| = 9$

26) **Answer:** $\frac{25}{x^7}$

$\frac{x^7}{25} \Rightarrow$ reciprocal is: $\frac{25}{x^7}$

27) **Answer:** $(-2, \ 1)$.

$\begin{cases} -2x + y = 5 \\ 5x + 4y = -6 \end{cases} \Rightarrow$ Multiplication -4 in first equation

$\Rightarrow \begin{cases} 8x - 4y = -20 \\ 5x + 4y = -6 \end{cases}$

Add two equations together $\Rightarrow 13x = -26 \Rightarrow x = -2$; then: $y = 1$

28) **Answer: 20.**

Plug in 68 for F and then solve for C.

$C = \frac{5}{9}(F - 32) \Rightarrow C = \frac{5}{9}(68 - 32) \Rightarrow C = \frac{5}{9}(36) = 20$

29) **Answer:** $-7i - 26$.

We know that: $i = \sqrt{-1} \Rightarrow i^2 = -1$

$(-3 + 4i)(2 + 5i) = -6 - 15i + 8i + 20i^2 = -6 - 7i - 20 = -7i - 26$

30) Answer: $-\sqrt{3}$.

$$\tan\frac{4\pi}{6} = \frac{\sin\frac{2\pi}{3}}{\cos\frac{2\pi}{3}} = \frac{\frac{1}{2}}{\frac{\sqrt{3}}{2}} = -\sqrt{3}$$

31) Answer: $\frac{3}{x}$.

$$\left(\frac{f}{g}\right)(x) = \frac{f(x)}{g(x)} = \frac{9x - 36}{3x^2 - 12x} = \frac{9(x-4)}{3x(x-4)} = \frac{3}{x}$$

32) Answer: $(4, -5)$, $\sqrt{10}$.

$(x - h)^2 + (y - k)^2 = r^2 \Rightarrow$ center: (h, k) and radius: r

$(x - 4)^2 + (y + 5)^2 = 10 \Rightarrow$ center: $(4, -5)$ and radius: $\sqrt{10}$

33) Answer: $(x + 2)^2 + (y - 3)^2 = 4^2$.

Use formula of a circle in the coordinate plane:

$(x - h)^2 + (y - k)^2 = r^2 \Rightarrow$ center: (h, k) and radius: r

center: $(-2, 3) \Rightarrow h = -2, k = 3$

circumference $= 2\pi \Rightarrow$ circumference $= 2\pi r = 8\pi \Rightarrow r = 4$

$(x + 2)^2 + (y - 3)^2 = 4^2$

34) Answer: $\frac{1}{4}$.

$$\text{Probability} = \frac{number\ of\ desired\ outcomes}{number\ of\ total\ outcomes} = \frac{20}{23+20+12+25} = \frac{20}{80} = \frac{1}{4}$$

35) Answer: $4\frac{1}{2}$.

METHOD ONE

$\log_5(x + 3) - \log_5(x - 3) = 1$

Add $\log_5(x - 3)$ to both sides

$\log_5(x + 3) - \log_5(x - 3) + \log_5(x - 3) = 1 + \log_5(x - 3)$

$\log_5(x + 3) = 1 + \log_5(x - 3)$

Apply logarithm rule: $a = \log_b(b^a) \Rightarrow 1 = \log_5(5^1) = \log_5(5)$

then: $\log_5(x + 3) = \log_5(5) + \log_5(x - 3)$

Logarithm rule: $\log_c(a) + \log_c(b) = \log_c(ab)$

then: $\log_5(5) + \log_5(x - 3) = \log_5(5(x - 3))$

$\log_5(x + 3) = \log_5(5(x - 3))$

When the logs have the same base:

$\log_b(f(x)) = \log_b(g(x)) \Rightarrow f(x) = g(x)$

$(x + 3) = 5(x - 3) \implies x = \frac{18}{4} = \frac{9}{2}$

METHOD TWO:

We know that: $\quad \log_a b - \log_a c = \log_a \frac{b}{c}$ and $\log_a b = c \Rightarrow b = a^c$

Then: $\quad \log_5(x + 3) - \log_5(x - 3) = \log_5 \frac{x+3}{x-3} = 1 \Rightarrow \frac{x+3}{x-3} = 5^1 = 5 \Rightarrow x + 3 = $

$5(x - 3) \Rightarrow x + 3 = 5x - 15 \Rightarrow 5x - x = 3 + 15 \rightarrow 4x = 18 \Rightarrow x = \frac{9}{2}$

"End"

Made in the USA
Coppell, TX
12 February 2022

73496313R00136